THE BRITISH ISLES, VOL. 1: ENGLAND

Guides to Dutch Atlas Maps
Editors: Peter van der Krogt & Elger Heere

I   The British Isles, vol. 1: England

Forthcoming:
Africa
America
Asia, vol. 1
Asia, vol. 2
Austria/Hungary
Baltic/Russia
France, vol. 1
France, vol. 2/Switzerland
Germany, vol. 1
Germany, vol. 2
Greece/Balkan
Historical maps (incl. Ptolemy /Peutinger)
Italy, vol. 1
Italy, vol. 2
Italy, vol. 3
Scandinavia
Spain/Portugal
The British Isles, vol. 2: Wales, Scotland and Ireland

Peter van der Krogt & Elger Heere

The British Isles, vol. 1: England

GUIDES TO DUTCH ATLAS MAPS
I

HES & DE GRAAF PUBLISHERS

OAK KNOLL PRESS

Illustration cover: 'Anglia, Scotia et Hibernia' from Gerard Mercator, *Atlas Sive Cosmographicae Meditationes de Fabrica Mundi et Fabricati Figura*, 1619 (Provided by the University Library of Amsterdam, UVA).

Published by:

HES & DE GRAAF Publishers BV
P.O. Box 540, 3990 GH Houten, Netherlands
www.hesdegraaf.com

and

Oak Knoll Press
310 Delaware Street, New Castle, DE, USA
www.oakknoll.com

ISBN 978 90 6194 390 7 (HES & DE GRAAF Publishers)
ISBN 978 1 58456 300 6 (Oak Knoll Press)

1. Introduction

This book offers a descriptive catalogue of all the maps of England, and particular parts of the country, published in Dutch atlases between 1570 and 1650. This means that all the maps in the atlases of Ortelius, Mercator-Hondius, Janssonius, Blaeu and their followers are recorded here.

This introduction gives the definition of an atlas, followed by short biographies of the most important Dutch atlas publishers of the era. The catalogue of maps is preceded by a guide to the descriptions and a comprehensive list of the atlases cited.

The text of this introduction is based entirely on the first three volumes of Koeman's *Atlantes Neerlandici*, edited by Peter van der Krogt.[1]

What is an atlas?

An atlas is broadly defined as a book with maps, which has the following characteristics:

(1) It is a collection of printed maps in book form or bound similarly to a book with a printed title page. In cases where text is included, the publisher's intention is to give the dominance of graphic elements (particularly maps, plans or town views) over textual elements. This must be clear, either from the title (whether expressed by the word 'atlas' or not) or from the concept of the work.

(2) There is a rough uniformity of map format, design and presentation throughout the work, and

(3) There is standardization (generally), from copy to copy in each edition, of the composition and arrangement of the components.

---

1   P. van der Krogt, *Atlantes Neerlandici*, vol. 1-3. 't Goy-Houten: HES & DE GRAAF Publishers, 1997-2003.

2. Biographies of Dutch atlas publishers

1 Abraham Ortelius (1527-1598)

The maker of the 'first atlas', the *Theatrum Orbis Terrarum* (1570), started his career as a colourist of maps. Later, he became a seller of books, prints and maps. His scientific and collecting interests developed in harmony with the spirit of a merchant. He was first and foremost a historian. Geography for him was the 'eye of history', which may explain why, in addition to coins and historical objects, he also collected maps. On the basis of his extensive travels through Europe and with the help of his international circle of friends, Ortelius was able to build a collection of the most up-to-date maps available.

During the last years of his life, he prepared a reduced engraved edition of the so-called Peutinger map for publication. He was never to see its appearance, however, for he died at Antwerp on 4 July 1598. The engraved version of the Peutinger map was included in the final and most complete edition of Ortelius's historical atlas, the *Parergon*, posthumously published in 1624 (31:711).

The unique position held by Ortelius's *Theatrum* in the history of cartography is to be attributed primarily to its qualification as 'the world's first regularly produced atlas'. Its great commercial success enabled it to make a significant contribution to 'geographical culture' throughout Europe at the end of the sixteenth century (Skelton, 1968). Its shape and contents set the standard for later atlases, when the centre of the map trade moved from Antwerp to Amsterdam. The characteristic feature of the *Theatrum* is that it consists of two elements; text and maps. Another important aspect is that it was the first undertaking of its kind to reduce the best available maps to a uniform format. To that end, maps of various formats and styles had to be generalised, just as the modern atlas publisher of today would do. In selecting maps for his compilation, Ortelius was guided by his critical spirit and his encyclopaedic knowledge of maps. But Ortelius did more than the atlas makers of today: he mentioned the names of the authors of the original maps and added the names of many other cartographers and geographers to his list. This 'Catalogus auctorum tabularum geographicarum', printed in the *Theatrum,* is one of the major peculiarities of the atlas. Ortelius and his successors kept his list of map authors up to date. In the first edition of 1570, the list included 87 names. In the posthumous edition of 1603, it contained 183 names.

Abraham Ortelius himself drew all his maps in manuscript before passing them to the engravers. In the preface to the *Theatrum* he stated that all the plates were engraved by Frans Hogenberg (last sentence of the address to the reader, f. C1r in atlas 31:001A: 'Vale, & fruere; atque Francisci Hogenbergi artificiosæ manui, cuius vnius indefatigabili diligentia ferè omnes hæ Tabulæ cælatæ sunt, bene faueto'). Hogenberg was probably assisted by the brothers Ambrosius and Ferdinand Arsenius (= Aertsen). The first edition of the *Theatrum* is dated 20 May 1570 and includes fifty-three maps.

The *Theatrum* was printed at Ortelius's expense first by Gielis Coppens van Diest, an Antwerp printer who had experience with printing cosmographical and cartographical works. From 1539 onwards, Van Diest had printed various editions of Apianus's *Cosmographia*, edited by Gemma Frisius, and in 1552 he printed Honterus's *Rudimentorum Cosmographicorum... Libri IIII* (see § 382). Gielis Coppens van Diest was succeeded as printer of the *Theatrum* in 1573 by his son Anthonis, who in turn was followed by Gillis van den Rade, who printed the 1575 edition. From 1579 onwards Christoffel Plantin (Plantijn) printed the *Theatrum*, still at Ortelius's own expense. Plantin and later his successors continued printing the work until Ortelius's heirs sold the copperplates and the publication rights in 1601 to Jan Baptist Vrients, who added some new maps. After 1612, the year of Vrients's death, the copperplates passed to the Moretus brothers, the successors of Christoffel Plantin.

The editions of the *Theatrum* may be subdivided into five groups on the basis of the number of maps. The first group contains fifty-three maps. In 1573, eighteen maps were added. The second group has seventy maps (one of the 18 new maps replaced a previous one). In 1579 another expansion was issued with twenty-three maps, bringing the total to ninety-three. The third addition occurred in 1584, again comprising twenty-three maps. Some maps replaced older ones, so as of that date the *Theatrum* contained 112. In 1590 a fourth addition followed with twenty-two maps. The editions then had 134 maps. A final, fifth expansion with seventeen maps followed in 1595, bringing the total to 151.

Abraham Ortelius was very customer-oriented with his additions. He waited until a reasonable number of new maps was ready for publication and added them at all at once to a new edition. He also sold the new maps as a separate set as a supplement to earlier editions of his atlas. These supplements, called in Latin *Additamenta*, were published in Latin, German and French (only the first and third are known), and probably also in Dutch.

2   Gerard Mercator (1512-1594)

Gerard de Cremer, who latinized his name to Gerard Mercator, 'the Ptolemy of our time' as he was called by Abraham Ortelius, was born on 5 March 1512 at Rupelmonde near Antwerp. His parents, Hubert and Emerentia de Cremer, lived in Gangelt in the county of Jülich, but in 1512 they were visiting Gisbert de Cremer, Hubert's brother, who was a priest at the Rupelmonde hospital.

In 1530 Gerard Mercator began attending the University of Leuven. There he devoted himself to the study of philosophy and took courses in mathematics, both theoretical and practical, under the guidance of Gemma Frisius. He was soon recognised as an expert in the construction of mathematical instruments, as a land surveyor and a cartographer. He also became qualified as a copper engraver, a skill he probably learned in the workshop of Gaspard van der Heyden. The first record of his work as an engraver – and also the first time his name appears on a cartographic work – is on Gemma Frisius's terrestrial globe (circa 1636): 'Gerardus Mercator Rupelmondanus coelavit cum Gaspare a Myrica' (Gerard Mercator from Rupelmonde engraved it with Gaspard van der Heyden), and on the celestial counterpart of 1537.

The same year, 1537, Gerard Mercator published his first map: the six-sheet wall map of the Holy Land, *Amplissima Terrae Sanctae Descriptio*. In 1538 he published a single-sheet world map using a double-cordiform projection (the so-called 'Orbis Imago'), followed two years later by a nine-sheet wall map of Flanders. Mercator was the first in history to introduce the italic handwriting to this domain (his booklet on italic handwriting was written and published in 1540).

Much of Mercator's income was derived from the construction and sale of globes. His terrestrial globe (diameter 41 cm) appeared in 1541, with the celestial globe appearing in 1551. The reason for publishing a terrestrial globe soon after those of his teacher Gemma Frisius was (except perhaps for purely commercial reasons) that Mercator was dissatisfied with the way in which most geographers had incorporated the Portuguese discoveries in the East Indies into the Ptolemaic world image. The 1541 and 1551 globes represent a milestone in globe production. Through their great commercial success and large distribution, the concept of globes in pairs became the standard for the next three centuries.

In 1552 Gerard Mercator moved with his family to the city of Duisburg in the Duchy of Kleve, perhaps because of the high degree of religious freedom which prevailed there. It is also likely that he was motivated by his knowledge of the plans to found a university in Duisburg. During the first ten years of his stay at Duisburg, Mercator was often employed as a land surveyor. His cartographical work of the Duisburg period includes the wall map of Europe, 1554; the map of Lorraine, c. 1564 (of which no copy is known to survive); the wall map of the British Isles, 1564; and the famous twenty-one-sheet world map with increasing latitudes, 1569.

Around 1563 Mercator became cosmographer in the service of the Duke William V of Jülich, Kleve, Berg etc. (1516–1592). As the duke's cosmographer Mercator felt obliged to write a cosmography, a description of the world in all its aspects. In the foreword to the *Chronologia*, published in 1568 and forming part of the cosmography, Mercator explained his plans for this project. It would consist of five volumes: 1. the creation, 2. the heavens, 3. geography (in three parts: a. modern maps, b. Ptolemaic maps, and c. historical maps), 4. history, and 5. chronology. The exact compilation of these volumes seems to have changed in later years. In 1595, his biographer, Walter Ghym, described the contents of the volumes differently.

According to Ghym, the title of Mercator's cosmography should be *Atlas, sive Cosmographicae Speculationis Libri Quinque.* Writing the text, drawing the maps, and cutting the plates required more of his time than he could afford. During the rest of his life Mercator completed only a few parts of his cosmography: the maps to Ptolemy's *Geographia* (1578), and four parts of the section with modern maps, including the appropriate texts (1585–89; 1:001 and 1:002). Gerard Mercator died on 2 December 1594, leaving the responsibility of finishing the cosmography to his son Rumold. The *Atlas Sive Cosmographicae Meditationes de Fabrica Mundi et Fabricati Figura,* as published by Rumold Mercator in 1595 (see below, 1:011), was still incomplete, lacking maps of Spain and detailed maps of the continents. (Note the slight difference between this title and the title as given by Ghym). After Rumold's death in 1599, the *Atlas* was reissued unaltered in 1602 (1:012).

Gerard's grandson, Gerard Mercator junior, had his grandfather's library sold by auction in Leiden in 1604. The copperplates for the maps of both the edition of Ptolemy and the *Atlas* were probably sold before the auction privately to Jodocus Hondius and Cornelis Claesz. of Amsterdam.

3   Hondius & Janssonius

3a *Jodocus Hondius (1563-1612)*

Joost de Hondt was born at Wakken (Flanders) in 1563, the son of Olivier de Hondt and Petronella d'Haverthuyn. Two years after Joost's birth, Olivier, who was an architect and alderman at Wakken, settled with his family in Gent. The young Joost displayed a great gift for drawing and calligraphy. Through study and lessons, he developed his talents, while his father added to his son's knowledge of mathematics, Greek, Latin, and 'the true Christian religion' (the Protestant faith). Joost soon had a good reputation as an engraver and was also celebrated in the fields of drawing and calligraphy. Probably for religious reasons, he rejected an offer by Alexander Farnese, Duke of Parma, to continue his studies in Rome. The capture of Gent by the Duke of Parma in September 1584 upset the future that seemed to be awaiting Joost. With many other Protestant inhabitants, he had to leave town and sail for England.

In London, Hondius settled down as an engraver and instrument maker. He possessed an ideal combination of personal qualities: in addition to his artistic and business skills, he had an interest in mathematics, geography and astronomy (later, in 1602, he would enroll as a student of liberal arts at the university of Leiden). During his stay in London he made the acquaintance of the most prominent English scholars and explorers of the time. In 1587, he married Colette van den Keere, sister of the well-known engraver, Pieter van den Keere (Petrus Kaerius; c. 1570/71–after 1646); some years earlier Hondius's sister, Jacomina, had married Pieter van den Berg (Petrus Montanus; c. 1560–1625). Jodocus Hondius co-operated closely with his two brothers-in-law. The first cartographical works by Jodocus Hondius date from circa 1588 – three maps for *The Mariners Mirrour*, the English version of Lucas Jansz. Waghenaer's *Spieghel der Zeevaerdt*. In the following years Hondius engraved several other maps and portraits. His principal London work is the engraving of the copperplates for the pair of globes by Emery Molyneux (1592-93); as engraver, Hondius was responsible for the decorative element of these globes.

The political situation in the Northern Netherlands in 1593 was such that Jodocus Hondius and his brothers-in-law were attracted to Amsterdam, where so many southern scholars, publishers and engravers had gone. In Amsterdam, they met refugees from the religious oppression in the southern provinces. Among them was Petrus Plancius (1522–1622), a minister as well as being an important cartographer and one of the initiators of the Dutch expeditions to the East Indies, and Cornelis Claesz. (died 1609), the most important Amsterdam publisher of geographical and cartographical works at the turn of the century. In this new centre of cartography, Jodocus Hondius set up his business 'In de Wackere Hondt' on the Kalverstraat, where many famous works were produced. His first dated work from Amsterdam is the 1593 map of the Seventeen Provinces. In 1595 he published a book on calligraphy titled *Theatrum Artis Scribendi*. Together with his brother-in-law Pieter van den Keere, he engraved a fifteen-sheet wall map of Europe (1595), the small maps for the *Caert-Thresoor*, and other maps. In the 1590s he also began to make globes, almost simultaneously with Willem Jansz. Blaeu, starting a competition which continued between their successors for more than eighty years.

Around 1604 Jodocus Hondius and Cornelis Claesz. acquired the Mercator copperplates. This acquisition was a turning point in Hondius's business. With these plates in 1605 Hondius and Claesz. published a new edition of Ptolemy's *Geographia,* edited by Hondius's brother-in-law Petrus Montanus – the first book printed in Amsterdam with Greek text. The next year they published a completely revised edition of Gerard Mercator's *Atlas* (1:101 and following); Hondius completed the unfinished *Atlas,* not only with thirty-six new maps to fill the omissions in Mercator's 1595 edition, but also added a new Latin text – written by Petrus Montanus – to Mercator's texts. During the preparation of the publication of Mercator's large *Atlas*, Jodocus had the size of the maps reduced in order to publish them as the *Atlas Minor* in 1607. For this venture, he cooperated not only with Cornelis Claesz., but also with Jan Jansz. from Arnhem (whose son, also named Jan Jansz., later, after Jodocus Hondius's death, married the latter's daughter).

In the first decade of the seventeenth century Hondius evolved from an engraver working on commission to a publisher of atlases and globes. After the death in 1609 of his co-publisher, Cornelis Claesz., Hondius continued on his own. Jodocus Hondius died unexpectedly in 1612 after a four-day illness. The date of his death, 'XIV Kal. Martii Anno MDCXII' (17 February 1612) is mentioned in the text of the Mercator-Hondius double portrait, inserted from 1613 onwards in the various editions of the *Atlas*.

3b Jodocus Hondius junior., Henricus Hondius and Johannes Janssonius

After 1612 the business was continued by Jodocus Hondius's widow Colette van den Keere, his son-in-law Johannes Janssonius, and later, his sons, Jodocus and Henricus. Very little is known about the cooperation between the Hondius brothers and their brother-in-law in publishing. Aside from the partnership in the continuation of Jodocus senior's workshop, it seems all three successively started their own businesses. The two brothers continued the business in their father's house on the Kalverstraat until around 1620.

In 1621, Jodocus Hondius junior (1593–1629) married Anna Staffmaeckers and moved into a shop on the Dam. There he started a business of his own, leaving his father's atlas business mainly to his younger brother. In 1618-19 he cooperated with the Leiden publisher Isaac Elsevier (1596–1651) in the publication of the historical atlas, *Theatrum Geographiae Veteris*, compiled by Petrus Bertius (1565–1629), professor of mathematics and librarian at the university of Leiden. Bertius also belonged to the Hondius 'clan', being the step-brother as well as brother-in-law of Pieter van den Keere (Jodocus junior's uncle). Bertius's historical atlas consisted of Mercator's Ptolemy maps and fourteen historical maps, partly borrowed from Abraham Ortelius's *Parergon*, partly engraved by Pieter van den Keere after the *Parergon* maps. Jodocus junior and Henricus jointly owned the copperplates of the globes, since the 1627 edition has both names in the imprint. Together with his brother-in-law Janssonius, Jodocus made a new large pair of globes (diameter 44 cm) in 1623. In 1626 he published *Nova et Accurata Italiae Hodiernae Descriptio*, a description of Italy with thirty-one small maps (16 x 23 cm) and sixty-six town views interspersed between the pages. Jodocus Hondius junior wanted to publish a new atlas to compete with his brother's *Atlas*. Before he could realize his plans, however, he died in 1629.

One of the major events in the early history of commercial cartography in Amsterdam was the sale of the copperplates of Jodocus Hondius junior to Willem Jansz. Blaeu, the most important competitor of the Hondius-Janssonius firm. Blaeu replaced Jodocus Hondius junior's name with his own on the plates and the following year, 1630, he published them together with his own maps as an *Appendix* to the Mercator-Hondius *Atlas*. In order to compete with Blaeu, both Henricus Hondius and Johannes Janssonius published their own *Appendices* to the Mercator-Hondius *Atlas*; for these they ordered the engraving of plates identical to the ones bought by Blaeu (see section 1:2).

Jodocus senior's younger son, Henricus Hondius (c. 1596/7–1651), also established himself on the Dam, 'sub insigno Atlantis', after his marriage in 1625 to Jannetje Verspreet. He took over the Mercator-Hondius *Atlas*, publishing new editions in 1623 and 1628; he also published wall maps (e.g., in 1624 a new edition of Blaeu's four wall maps of the continents) and, together with his brother, the globes. After the death of his brother Jodocus and his mother (both of whom died in 1629), Henricus moved back to his father's house. Henricus Hondius seems to have been the sole publisher of the *Atlas* from 1623 until 1633. The 1633 German edition is the first *Atlas* (1:313) with the name of Janssonius on the title page. Henricus was also associated with the Paris bookseller, Melchior Tavernier (1594–1665); several of his maps of France bear the additional address: 'Et se vendent a Paris chez Melchior Tavernier a la Sphere'. Until the early 1640s the names of both Hondius and Janssonius appeared on the title page; afterwards, Hondius's name disappeared.

Johannes Janssonius (the latinised version of Jan Jansz.) (1588–1664) was the son of the Arnhem publisher Jan Jansz. In August 1612 Johannes married Elisabeth Hondius, the daughter of Jodocus Hondius. After his marriage he established himself as a publisher of cartographic material, occasionally in cooperation with his brothers-in-law. He entered into serious competition with Willem Jansz. Blaeu when he copied Blaeu's *Licht der Zeevaert* after the expiration of the privilege in 1620. In the 1620s Janssonius entered the globe business, first by making a new globe on his own (1620), later by co-publishing with Jodocus Jr. the pair of 44 cm. globes (1623), and by taking over the globes from his uncle Pieter van den Keere. In 1631 he began publishing atlases together with Henricus Hondius.

In the early 1640s Henricus Hondius left the atlas publishing business completely to Janssonius. Competition with Joan Blaeu, Willem's son and successor, in atlas production prompted Janssonius to enlarge his *Atlas Novus* finally into a work of six volumes, into which an atlas of the seas and an atlas of the Old World were inserted. Other atlases published by Janssonius are; Mercator's *Atlas Minor*, from 1628 to 1651 (in Latin, French, Dutch and German), Georg Hornius's *Accuratissima Orbis Antiqui Delineatio* beginning in 1652 (section 1:6), the 'townbooks' in eight volumes (1657) (these will be described in volume 4 of *Koeman's Atlantes Neerlandici)*, Andreas Cellarius's *Atlas Coelestis seu Harmonia Macrocosmica* (section 1:8) and several sea atlases and pilot guides. In addition to his cartographic publication, Janssonius had a large publishing company producing a wide variety of books, with offices in several parts of Europe. Janssonius died in 1664.

3c *Janssonius's heirs and successors in atlas publishing*

The heirs of Johannes Janssonius were the children of his son Jodocus Janssonius (c. 1613/14–1655), and his daughters Elisabeth (married to Johannes van Waesbergen) and Maria (married to Johannes van Almeloveen). Each of the heirs received a third of the estate. However, the ownership of certain of the books could not be divided during the six years that followed Janssonius's death in order for them to continue being printed; the *Atlas Major,* the *Atlas Minor*, and the townbooks. The shop operated for another three years under the management of Van Waesbergen.

Johannes Janssonius van Waesbergen (c. 1616/17–1681), son of Johan van Waesbergen, a printer in Rotterdam, and Maria van der Hoeven, married Elisabeth Janssonius in 1642. In 1661, Van Waesbergen was already referred to as a fellow-bookseller of his father-in-law. Together with the Amsterdam bookseller, Steven Swart, and Moses Pitt he ventured in 1680 into the failed publication of *The English Atlas*. As 'Janssonio Waesbergianos' his name is found on the 1677 and 1684 editions of Hornius's historical atlas (1:606 and 1:607). After his death in 1681 his widow authorised her two sons to take charge of the business in her name. These sons were Johannes Janssonius van Waesbergen junior and Gillis Janssonius van Waesbergen (in 1677 the latter had married his cousin Susanna Janssonius, daughter of his mother's brother Jodocus Janssonius). In 1682, Gillis authorised his brother Johannes to carry on the business on his own, since Gillis had settled in Danzig, where he set up a business.

On 9 June 1694 the Janssonius van Waesbergen brothers auctioned the Janssonius copperplates. To be sold were 'all the copperplates belonging to the atlas and the townbooks of the late Johannes Janssonius, which contains three volumes more than any other published atlas, to wit the Water World, the Old World and the Celestial World; with these [the buyer is] able to print a most complete atlas'. Also available were 'complete atlases of the late Johannes Janssonius in Latin, French and Dutch; also some parts in the English language'. The plates were bought by Petrus Schenk (1661–1711) and Gerard Valk (1652–1726), who added their names to the plates of the Janssonius maps and published them in their own atlases. In 1708 they published a new edition of Cellarius's celestial atlas (1:802).

The copperplates for the Ptolemaic maps, engraved by Mercator in 1578 and last published by Isaac Elsevier and Jodocus Hondius junior in 1618-19, seem to have been acquired in 1694 by François Halma (1653–1722), since, in cooperation with several other publishers, he published new editions in 1695, 1698 and 1704. For these editions the plates were modernised with new cartouches. After Halma's death the 150-year-old plates were used once more in 1730, with an added graticule, for the Wetstein & Smith edition of Ptolemy's maps.

Despite the 1694 sale, the 1700 English edition of Hornius's historical atlas (1:611) and the 1701 war atlas (1:901) still bear the names of both Janssonius van Waesbergen brothers in the imprint. Later editions of Hornius's atlas were published by Pieter de Hondt (1696–1764), the most prominent book seller and publisher in The Hague. It is not known where De Hondt acquired the copperplates for this atlas (he was not connected with the Hondius family, whose Dutch name also was De Hondt). De Hondt's 1740 and 1741 editions (1:613, 1:621 and 1:631) are the latest works included in this first volume of *Koeman's Atlantes Neerlandici*.

4   The Blaeus

4a *Willem Jansz. Blaeu and his sons*

Willem Jansz. Blaeu came from a rather prosperous Amsterdam Anabaptist family. His father lived in Alkmaar, where he was a herring merchant, rather than Amsterdam. Willem was born either in Alkmaar or in the nearby village of Uitgeest in 1571, and it was there that he received his early schooling. During this period he must have met Adriaen Anthonisz. (1541–1620), surveyor, astronomer and superintendent of fortification construction of the United Provinces. Adriaen Anthonisz.'s son, Adrianus Metius, who was also born in 1571, would later become

Blaeu's scientific advisor. As a young man, Blaeu went to Amsterdam to work in the office of his cousin by marriage, Cornelis Pietersz. Hooft, to be trained to be a herring merchant like his father, but he was more interested in scientific matters, especially astronomy. In 1595, he left for Denmark to study astronomy with Tycho Brahe on the island of Ven. After his return he published his first cartographic work – a celestial globe according to the observations of Tycho Brahe – which had been commissioned by Adriaen Anthonisz.

About 1597, Blaeu married Maertgen Cornelisdr. from Uitgeest: of this marriage three sons (Joan, Pieter and Cornelis) and two daughters (Stijntje and Sijtche) were born.

Willem Jansz. Blaeu moved to Amsterdam in 1598 or 1599 and at first manufactured only globes and instruments. In 1603, he began to manufacture other cartographic products and navigational instruments and to publish books. His first maps, which appeared in 1604, were folio maps of the Seventeen Provinces and of the county of Holland, and a world map in two sheets. In 1608, he published a pilot guide, *Het Licht der Zeevaert.*

In 1618 another map maker, bookseller and publisher, Jan Jansz. (Johannes Janssonius) established himself on the Damrak next door to Blaeu's shop. It is no wonder that these two neighbours, who began accusing each other of copying and stealing their information, became fierce competitors who never had a good word to say about each other. In about 1621 Willem Jansz. (Guilelmus Janssonius in its Latin version) decided to put an end to the confusion between his name and his competitor's, and assumed his grandfather's sobriquet, 'blauwe Willem' ('blue Willem'), as the family name; thereafter he called himself Willem Jansz. Blaeu.

In 1621 – the same year Blaeu's privilege on his pilot guide *Het Licht der Zeevaert* ended – Janssonius published a plagiarised copy of it. It is perhaps this act by his competitor that gave Blaeu the idea of competing with his opponent in the area where Janssonius and his brother-in-law Henricus Hondius had a monopoly, namely atlas production. Blaeu started to gather maps for his own atlas, although he had already published several maps in atlas format (he may already have had plans by then to publish an atlas). After purchasing the copperplates of the atlas maps produced by Jodocus Hondius junior, Blaeu brought out his first atlas in 1630. With this publication he began a new trend in Amsterdam atlas production, characterised by competition and an increase in the number of maps. Blaeu's first altas was the *Atlantis Appendix sive Pars Altera*, a modest atlas without text and with only sixty maps. A year later he published a second *Appendix* with Latin text and almost 100 maps. It appears that this new competition prompted Henricus Hondius, in cooperation with his brother-in-law Johannes Janssonius, to publish a considerably enlarged new edition of the French-language *Atlas* in 1633. It now consisted of two volumes and included 238 maps. The same year, the first German-language edition was published, containing 'only' 161 maps. A Dutch-language edition, *Atlas ofte Afbeeldinghe vande Gantsche Weerldt,* with 182 maps, followed in 1634 (atlas 1:331 in volume 1 of *Koeman's Atlantes Neerlandici).*

Blaeu's plans to publish an entirely new atlas of the world were first revealed in a newspaper report of 11 February 1634. On that day, the *Courante uyt Italien ende Duytschlandt* of Jan van Hilten reported: 'In Amsterdam at Willem Jansz. Blaeu's is printing at present the great map-book the Atlas, in four languages; Latin, French, High and Low German. The High German will appear by Easter, the Low German and the French in the first coming month of May, or at the latest at the beginning of June, and the Latin shortly afterwards: all on very fine paper, wholly renewed with newly cut plates and new extensive descriptions.' Willem Jansz. Blaeu and his son Joan could not, however, realise these plans in 1634; only the German edition appeared in that year. The two-volume editions of the atlas in the other three languages were not published until 1635.

The extent of Blaeu's ambitious plans for a world atlas is reflected in his preface, where he stated that it was his intention to describe the whole world and to depict all the ports and seas, and therefore several other volumes of the atlas were to follow shortly. In view of these plans, Blaeu's investment in a new printing shop is not surprising.

Willem Jansz. Blaeu died in October 1638, leaving his prospering business to his sons, Joan and Cornelis.

4b Joan Blaeu (ca. 1597/98-1673) and Cornelis Blaeu (ca. 1610-1642)

Joan Blaeu, born in Alkmaar in 1597 or 1598, studied law and mathematics at the University of Leiden from 1615 to 1618, and travelled to Italy to finish his education. From around 1630 he cooperated with his father in the printing and publishing business, and after his father's death he and his brother Cornelis took over the book trade and printing business. After Cornelis's death in March 1642, the business was left to Joan Blaeu.

In 1638, Joan was appointed his father's successor at the hydrographic office of the Dutch East India Company (VOC). His promotion of maritime cartography lacked the fervour with which he appropached geography. He aimed at a total description of the heavens, the earth and the seas, a goal that was unachievable, but his efforts culminated in the publication of the *Atlas Maior* and the town books of the Netherlands and of Italy.

The publication of Blaeu's *Atlas Maior* was the climax of Dutch atlas production. It was less than a century since the first modern world atlas, Ortelius's *Theatrum Orbis Terrarum,* a volume with fifty maps, had appeared. Blaeu's atlas consisted of 600 maps in nine to twelve volumes. Because of the frequent use of Mercator's title *Atlas,* this word became the general word for a collection of maps bound in a volume. By the time the *Atlas Maior* appeared, atlases were a common product of most map producing firms.

On 23 February 1672 a fire ruined Blaeu's printing house. One year later, Joan Blaeu died. The fire and the passing away of the director led to a sale of the stock of the Blaeu firm. Five public auctions (four in 1674, one in 1677) dispersed the printed books, maps, atlases, globes, and the copperplates among several map dealers and publishers in Amsterdam. Most of this material was acquired by a number of booksellers acting in partnership (for example, Wolfgang and Boom). Volume 5 of *Koeman's Atlantes Neerlandici* will deal with the further history of Blaeu's copperplates for atlas maps.

4c *Joan Blaeu's sons: Willem, Pieter, and Joan II Blaeu*

As a result of Joan Blaeu's death, the remaining printing department was left in the hands of the Blaeu family. It was managed by the three sons of Joan Blaeu; Willem Blaeu (1635–1701), Pieter Blaeu (1637–1706), and Joan II Blaeu (1650–1712). Pieter Blaeu had become active in the management of the shop in 1662. After his father's death, Joan II Blaeu directed the printing house, and was appointed cartographer of the VOC. The role of the eldest son, Willem Blaeu, is unclear. In 1678 the book shop was sold and the brothers then concentrated on the printing business. They printed under the name "Joan Blaeu's Heirs", mainly for the company of Wolfgang, Janssonius van Waesbergen, Van Someren, Boom, and Goethals (the so-called Latin Company), founded in 1682. Joan II Blaeu joined this company in 1684. Since Janssonius van Waesbergen was the son-in-law of Johannes Janssonius, this company ended the competition between Janssonius and Blaeu and brought the two enterprises into cooperation. In 1695, the world-renowned Blaeu printing house came to an end with the sale of the firm's inventory at a public auction.

Descriptive catalogue

Notes for use

In this book, the map descriptions are given in a simplified ISBD format. The following fields are mentioned successively:

Order number

Map number, as it appears in the *Atlantes Neerlandici*.

Area description, in short a rough indication of the area of the map.

Title, as it appears on the map.

Translated title, translation of the, mostly, Latin titles in English.

Imprint, as it appears on the map.

Dimensions, height x width in centimetres, rounded off to the nearest half centimetre. The dimensions are taken from the printed image (including borders).

Notes, short information on the map, the mapped area, the atlas in which the map first appeared, or on the person to whom the map is dedicated.

Occurrence in atlases, a list of atlases in which the map occurs, with page numbers.

References to general cartobibliographies or literature. No attempt has been made to list all references.

I   **[5000:1A] British Isles**
ANGLIA, | SCOTIA et | HIBER- | NIA
England, Scotland and Ireland
Per Gerardum Mercatorem.
32.5 x 41 cm.

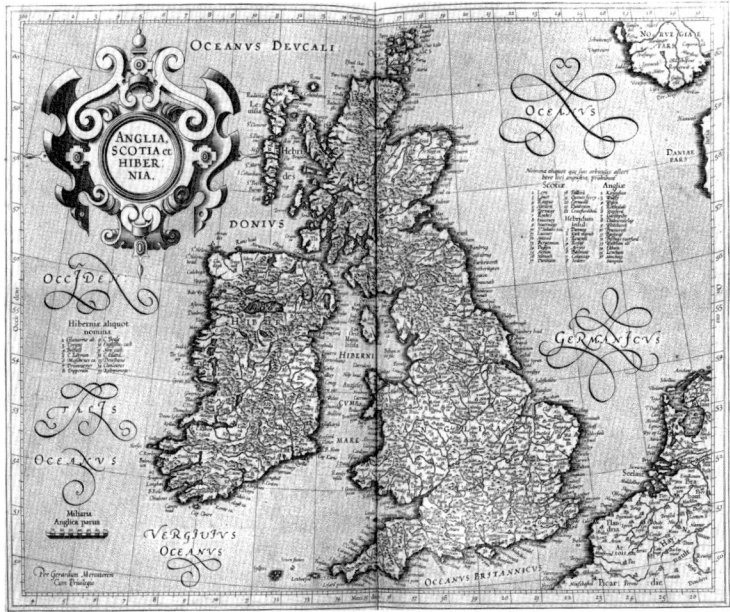

Notes   The maps for the *Atlas* of Gerard Mercator (1512–1594) – the first book with the title atlas – were published in five parts between 1585 and 1595. The fifth part (maps of the British Isles, Northern and Eastern Europe) was prepared for publication by Gerard's son Rumold Mercator in 1595. To the left of Ireland and the right of Scotland there are some explanations of the numbers in the map.

Occurrence in atlases
1:011/12 Atlas, Mercator, 1595: 8 III
1:101 Hondius-Claesz., 1606: 9 M 47-48
1:102 Atlas, Hondius-Claesz., 1607-08: 9 M 45-46
1:111 Atlas, Hondius, 1609: 9 M 45-46
1:103 Atlas, Hondius, 1611-12: 9 M 45-46
1:104 Atlas, Hondius jr, 1613-19: 9 P 45-46
1:112 Atlas, Hondius jr, 1613-16: 9 N 51-52
1:113 Atlas, Hondius jr, 1619: 9 M 45-46
1:105 Atlas, Hondius, 1623: 9 P 45-46
1:114 Atlas, Hondius, 1628: 9 X 81-84
1:107 Atlas, Hondius, 1630: 9 P 45-46

References   Shirley 1991, no. 180.

2   [5000:1B] British Isles
**ANGLIAE, SCOTIAE, ET HIBERNIAE, SIVE | BRITANNICAR:
INSULARUM DESCRIPTIO**
Map of England, Scotland and Ireland or the British Isles
Amstelodami | Excudebat Ioannes | Ianßonius Anno | 1621
32 X 50 cm.

Notes   The first state of this map was published in 1604 by Pieter van den Keere.
Bottom right there are portraits of King James I of Scotland, Henry, prince of
Wales, and Queen Anne.

Occurrence in atlases
1:202 Appendix, Janssonius, 1630: 10 blank

References   Shirley 1991, no. 263 (Van den Keere's edition), 374 and 414.

3   [5000:1C] British Isles
Magnæ | BRITANNIÆ | et HIBERNIÆ | TABULA
Map of Great Britain and Ireland
Amstelodami | Ex Officina et sumptibus Henrici | Hondij. Ao.
Domini 1631
37.5 x 50 cm.

Notes   The inset map is a map of the Orkney Island. The first state of this map
was published in 1617 by Jodocus Hondius.

Occurrence in atlases
1:203 Appendix, Hondius, 1631: 10 blank
1:311 Atlas, Hondius, 1633: VI 9 X 81-84
1:321/22 Atlas, Janssonius-Hondius, 1633: 7 G 25-28
1:331 Atlas, Janssonius-Hondius, 1634: 5 E 9-10
1:341 Hondius-Janssonius, 1636-41: VI 5 Q 49-52
1:323 Newer Atlas, Janssonius, 1636: VI 9 G[2] 25-28
1:401 Atlas Novus, Janssonius-Hondius, 1638: VI 7 H
1:421/2 Newer Atlas, Janssonius, 1638: VI 6 C2
1:431 Nieuwen Atlas, Janssonius, 1638-44: VI 5 E-F
1:411/2 Nouveau Theatre du Monde, Hondius, 1639-42: VI 7 G
1:413 Nouveau Theatre du Monde, Janssonius, 1644-47: VI 7 G

References   Shirley 1991, no. 355a (Jodocus Jr.'s edition) and 435.

4 [5000:1D] **British Isles**
MAGNÆ | BRITANNIÆ | et | HIBERNIÆ | Nova | DESCRIPTIO
New map of Great Britain and Ireland
Amstelodami, | Apud Ioannem Ianßonium
43 X 53.5 cm.

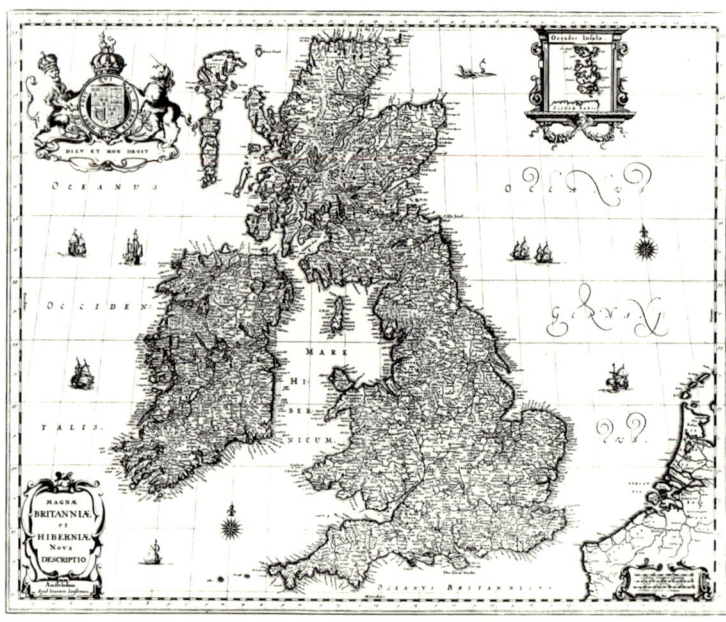

Notes   This map shows England, Scotland and Ireland. At the corner left above there is the royal coat of arms of the British monarch. Above right, there is an inset map of the Orkney Islands.

Occurrence in atlases
1:421/2 Newer Atlas, Janssonius, 1638: VI 6 C2
1:431 Nieuwen Atlas, Janssonius, 1638-44: VI 5 E-F
1:411/2 Nouveau Theatre du Monde, Hondius, 1639-42: VI 7 G
1:424/27 Atlas Novus, Janssonius, 1644-45: VI 5 F
1:433/36 Nieuwen Atlas, Janssonius, 1638-44/1658: VI 4 D
1:403/05 Atlas Novus, Janssonius, 1647/1657-62: V4 2 D 11-12
1:414/15 Le Nouvel Atlas... Tome Quatrieme, Janssonius, 1646-49: V4 2 E 15-16
1:425 Novus Atlas, Janssonius, 1647-49: V4 2 E 15-16
1:434/36 Nieuwen Atlas... Het Vierde deel, Janssonius, 1647-49/1658: V4 1 +
1:441 Nuovo Atlas, Janssonius, 1653-66: V4 57 A
1:407 Atlas Contractus, Janssonius, 1666: VI 74
1:408 Atlas, Janssonius, after c. 1680: V3 1

References   Shirley 1991, no. 487.

5.1   [5000:2.1] British Isles
MAGNÆ | BRITANNIÆ | et | HIBERNIÆ | TABVLA
Map of Great Britain and Ireland
AMSTELODAMI, | Guiljelmus Blaeuw excudit
46.5x55 cm (map 36.5x45 cm)

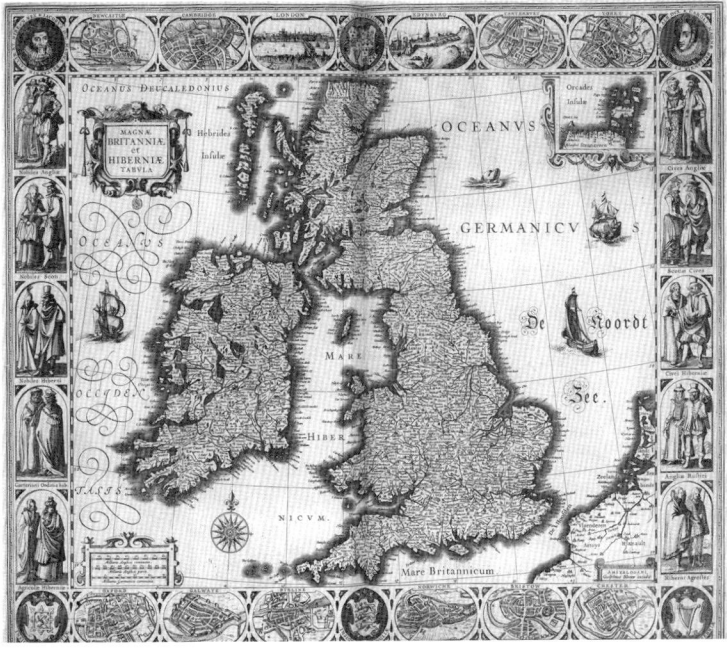

Notes   The edges of the map are decorated with drawings of towns (upper and lower borders) and costumes (left and right).

Occurrence in atlases
2:011 Atlantis Appendix, W.J. Blaeu, 1630: 7
2:021 Appendix Theatri... et Atlantis, W.J. Blaeu, 1631: 7 K

References   Schilder, MCN IV, no. 62.1-2.

5.2   [5000:2.2] British Isles
       MAGNÆ | BRITANNIÆ | et | HIBERNIÆ | TABVLA
       Map of Great Britain and Ireland
       AMSTELODAMI, | Guiljelmus Blaeuw excudit
       38.5 x 50 cm.

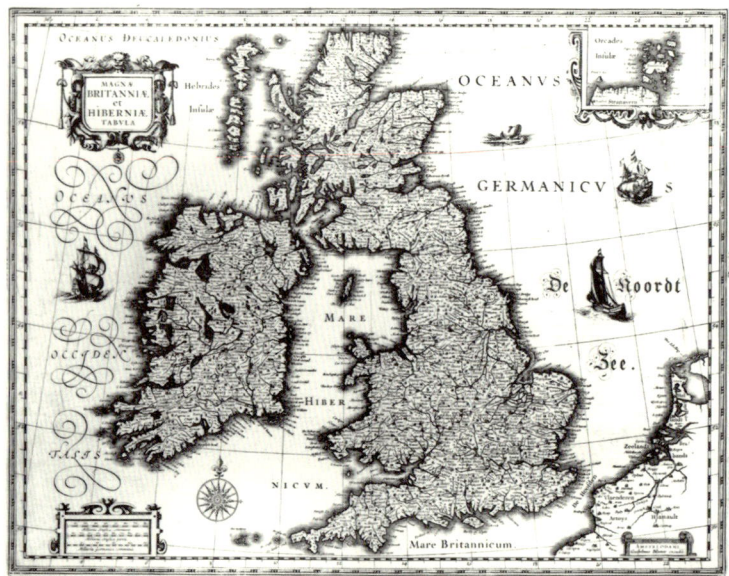

Notes   The original map from approximately 1629 had on all sides decorative
edges. When Blaeu included the map in 1631 in its atlas, the plate appeared too
large and he the edges of the map has cut. Remarkable is the drawing of the wall
of Hadrianus, which had to protect Roman England against the irruptions of the
Scots. The wall is 117 kilometers long and have been built for emperor Hadrianus,
who ordered its construction in 122 AD.

Occurrence in atlases
2:021 Appendix Theatri... et Atlantis, W.J. Blaeu, 1631: 7 K 17
2:011 Appendix Theatri ...et Atlantis, W.J. Blaeu, 1631: 7 K
2:131 Novus Atlas, W.J. Blaeu, 1634/35: vi 7 G
2:132 Novus Atlas, W.J. Blaeu, 1635: vi 7 G
2:132 Theatrum Orbis Terrarum, W.& J. Blaeu, 1635: vi 7 K
2:111-12 Le Theatre du Monde, W. & J. Blaeu, 1635: vi 8 K
2:121 Toonneel des Aerdrycks, W. & J. Blaeu, 1635: vi 101 2Y
2:201 Theatrum Orbis Terrarum, W. & J. Blaeu, 1640: v3 63 A 1
2:211 Theatre du Monde ou Nouvel Atlas, J. & C. Blaeu, 1640-43: v3 63 A 1 or
STVXYy
2:221 Toonneel des Aerdrycks, J. & C. Blaeu, 1642-43: v3 63 A 1
2:231 Novus Atlas, J. & C. Blaeu, 1641-42: v3 63 A
2:212-3 Theatre du Monde ou Nouvel Atlas, J. Blaeu, 1643-45: v3 63 A 1

2:202-3 Theatrum Orbis Terrarum, J. Blaeu, 1644-45: v3 63 A 1

2:301 Theatrum Orbis Terrarum sive Atlas Novus Pars Quarta, J. Blaeu, 1646: 1 blank

2:302-3 Theatrum Orbis Terrarum sive Atlas Novus Pars Quarta, J. Blaeu, 1646-48: 1 A 1-2

2:311 Le Theatre du Monde ou Nouvel Atlas, Quatriesme Partie, J. Blaeu: 1 blank

2:312 Cinquème Volume de la Geographie Blaviane, J. Blaeu, 1663-67: 1 A 1-2

2:321 Toonneel des Aerdycks oft Nieuwe Atlas... Vierde deel, J. Blaeu, 1648: 1 A 1-2

2:322 Toonneel des Aerdycks oft Nieuwe Atlas... Vierde deel, J. Blaeu, 1648: 1 A 1-2

2:331 Novus Atlas and Atlas Major (Vierter Teil), J. Blaeu, 1645-48: 1 blank

2:232 Novus Atlas, J. Blaeu, 1647-49: v3 63 A

2:341 Nuevo Atlas del Reyno de Inglaterra, J. Blaeu, 1645/48: 1 A 1-2

References   Schilder, MCN IV, no. 62.3; Van der Krogt 2002 18:04.

6 **[5000:31A] British Isles**
ANGLIAE, SCOTIAE, ET HIBERNIAE, SIVE | BRITANNICAR:
INSVLARVM DESCRIPTIO.
Map of England, Scotland and Ireland or the British Isles
35 x 50.5 cm.

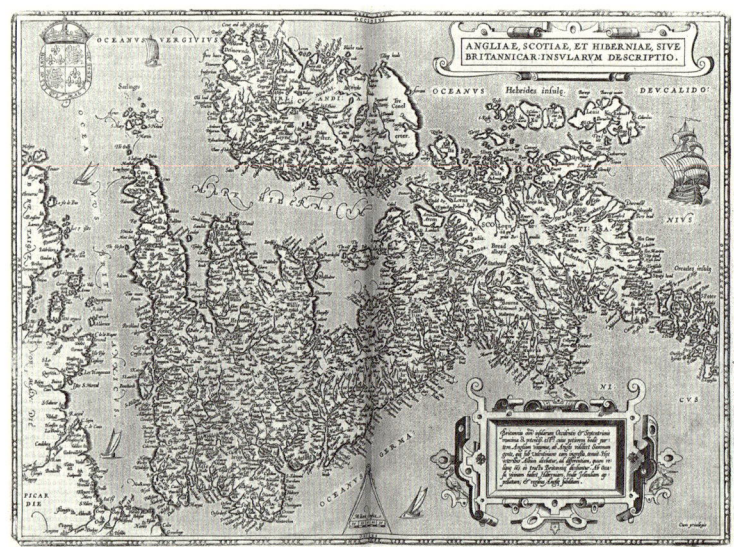

Notes This map first appeared in an edition of the *Theatrum Orbis Terrarum*
published by Coppens van Diest in Antwerp. Upper left there is an old coat of
arms of England.

Occurrence in atlases
31:001 Theatrum Orbis Terrarum, Coppens van Diest, 1570: 6 #6
31:002 Theatrum Orbis Terrarum, Coppens van Diest, 1571: 6 #6
31:101/111 Theatre oft Toonneel des Aerdtbodems, Coppens van Diest, 1571: 6 #6
31:301 Théatre de l´Universe, Plantin, 1587: 6 #6
31:201 Theatrum oder Schwaplatz des Erdbodems, Coppens van Diest, 1572: 6 #6
31:290 Theatrum Orbis Terrarum, Koler, 1572: 6
31:011 Theatrum Orbis Terrarum, Coppens van Diest, 1573: 6 #6
31:211 Theatrum oder Schawbüch der Ertkreijs, Plantin, 1580: 6 #6
31:012 Theatrum Orbis Terrarum, Coppens van Diest, 1574: 6 #6
31:311 Théatre de l'Univers, Coppens van Diest, 1574/72: 6 #6
31:013 Theatrum Orbis Terrarum, Van den Rade, 1575: 6 #6
31:021-022 Theatrum Orbis Terrarum, Plantin, 1579: 8 #8
31:211/022 Theatrum oder Schawbüch der Ertkreijs, Plantin, 1580: 8 #8
31:321 Théatre de l'Univers, Plantin, 1581: 8 #8
31:031 Theatrum Orbis Terrarum, Plantin, 1584: 9 #9
31:331 Théatre de l'Univers, Plantin, 1587: 9 #9
31:431 Theatro de la Tierra Universal, Plantin, 1588: 9 #9

31:041 Theatrum Orbis Terrarum, Plantin, 1592: 10 #10
31:051 Theatrum Orbis Terrarum, Plantin, 1595: 10 #10
31:051 Theatrum Orbis Terrarum, [Claesz.], 1598: 10 #10
31:351 Théâtre de l'Univers, Plantin, 1598: 10 #10
31:041 Theatrum Orbis Terrarum,Moretus, 1601: 10 #10
31:451 Theatro d'el Orbe de la Tierra, Vrients, 160210 #10
31:251 Theatrum oder Schawbuch der gantzen Welt, Vrients, 1602: 10 #10
31:041 Theatrum Orbis Terrarum, Vrients, 1603: 10 #10
31:551 The Theatre of the Whole World, Norton, 1606: 10 #10
31:651/652 Theatro del Mondo, Vrients, 1608/J. & B. Moretus, 1612: 10 #10
31:054/055 Theatrum Orbis Terrarum, Vrients, 1609/J. & B. Moretus, 1612: 10 #10
31:452-454 Theatro d'el Orbe de la Tierra, Vrienst, 1602/1609[1641]): 10 #10
31:122 Theatrum Orbis Terrarum, Vrients, 1598, J. Moretus, 1598: 10 #10

References   Van den Broecke 2011, 16; Karrow 1993, 1/11; Meurer 1991, 6; Shirley 1991 (Br. Isl. I), 86; Werner 1998, cat. no. 25.

7.1   [5000:31B.1] British Isles
ANGLIAE ET HIBERNIAE | ACCVRATA DESCRIPTIO, | VET-
ERIBVS ET RECENTIORIBVS | NOMINIBVS ILLVSTRATA:
ET AD D. GVLIEL. CAMDENI BRITANIAM ACCOMMODATA.
Accurate map of England and Ireland with the ancient and modern
names depicted to "Britania" by William Camden
Ioannes Baptista Vrints | Geographicarum tabularum | calcographus,
excud. Antuerpiæ.
44 X 56.5 cm.

Notes   The map is dedicated by John Baptist Vrients to King James I. The map
contains a genealogical table of the English monarchs from William the Con-
queror to James I.

Occurrence in atlases
31:551 The Theatre of the Whole World, Norton, 1606: 12 #12
31:651/652 Theatro del Mondo, Vrients, 1608/J. & B. Moretus, 1612: 12 #12

References   Van den Broecke 2011, 17.1; Meurer 1991, 148; Shirley 1991 (Br. Isl. I),
275.

7.2   [5000:31 B.2] British Isles
ANGLIAE ET HIBERNIAE | ACCVRATA DESCRIPTIO, | VET-
ERIBVS ET RECENTIORIBVS | NOMINIBVS ILLVSTRATA:
ET AD D. GVLIEL. CAMDENI BRITANIAM ACCOMMO-
DATA.
Accurate map of England and Ireland with the ancient and modern
names depicted to "Britania" by William Camden
Ioannes Baptista Vrints | Geographicarum tabularum | calcographus,
excud. Antuerpiæ.

Notes   The dedication has been removed from this second state of the map. The
information on King James I in the cartouche now reads: '1603 Iacobus Magnae
Britanniae Rex'.

Occurrence in atlases
31:651/652 Theatro del Mondo, Vrients, 1608/J. & B. Moretus, 1612: 12 #12
31:054/055 Theatrum Orbis Terrarum, Vrients, 1609/J. & B. Moretus, 1612: 12 #12
31:452-454 Theatro d'el Orbe de la Tierra, Vrienst, 1602/1609[1641]): 12 #12

References   Van den Broecke 2011, 17.2; Shirley 1991 (Br. Isl. I), 323.

8   [5000:32] **British Isles**
       ANGLIAE SCOTIAE ET HIBERNIE | NOVA DESCRIPTIO.
       New map of England, Scotland and Ireland
       35 X 50 cm.

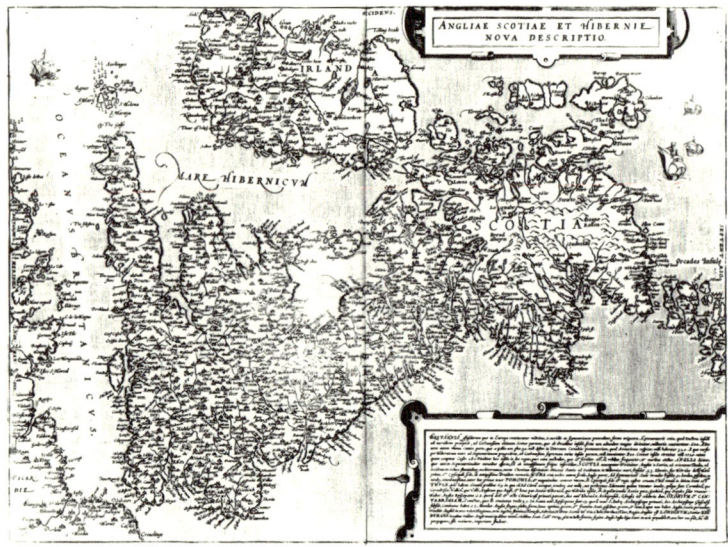

Notes   This map was published in both the 1578 and 1593 editions of the *Speculum* of Gerard de Jode. Part of the engraving of the atlas was done by himself, part by the brothers Jan and Lucas van Doetecum. It is very likely that Ortelius was responsible for a delay in the publication of Gerard de Jode's *Speculum*. Ortelius prevented the granting of the necessary approbations to De Jode, because he wanted to protect the commercial value of his *Theatrum Orbis Terrarum*, published in 1570.

Occurrence in atlases
32:01 Speculum Orbis Terrarum, De Jode, 1578: 26 XXVI 2c
32:02 Speculum Orbis Terrae, De Jode, 1593: 33 2I 32

References   Shirley 1991 (Br. Isl. I), 85 (1st state) and 119 (2nd state).

9   [5000:334] **British Isles**
[Map of the British Isles].
18 x 14 cm.

Notes   This map is a woodcut. The map is usually bound with the bottom at the right, suggesting that east is at the top. However, the names in the map show that one has to turn the map to get north at the top.

Occurrence in atlases
334:01 Le Miroir du Monde, Heyns, 1598: 9 G4r 26

References   Shirley 1991 (Br. Isl. I), 202.

10   [5000:342] **British Isles**
ANGLIA | SCOTIA et | Hibernia.
England, Scotland and Ireland
9.5 x 13.5 cm.

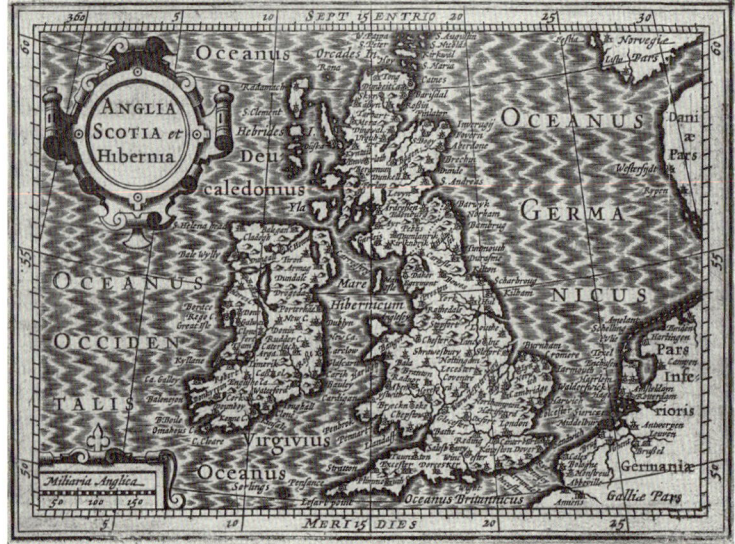

Notes   This map of England, Scotland and Ireland is from Petrus Bertius' *Tabularum Geographicorum Contractarum Libri...*, which followed Barent Langenes' *Caert Thresoor*. Bertius first applied texts for the Langenes atlas, but in 1616 he made his own pocket atlas.

Occurrence in atlases
342:01 Tabulae Geographicae Contractae, Bertius, 1616/18: 14 G1V 98
342:11 La Geographie Racourcie de Pierre Bertius, Hondius jr, 1618: 14 G1V 98
342:21 Atlas Minor, J. Blaeu, 1637: 73

References   Shirley 1991 (Br. Isl. I), 347.

11   [5000:351] **British Isles**
ANGLIA SCO- | TIA et HIBERNIA.
England, Scotland and Ireland
13.5 x 18 cm.

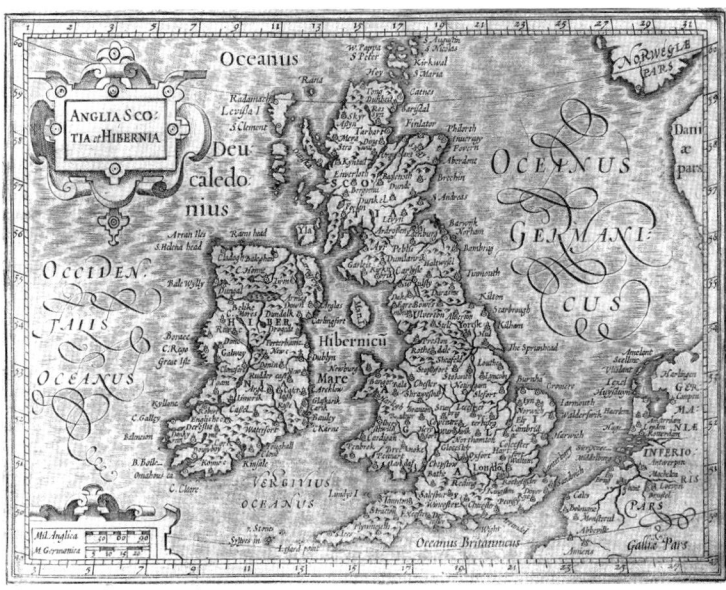

Notes   A year after publishing Mercator's *Atlas*, Jodocus Hondius engraved a
set of plates for a pocket edition. Ortelius's *Epitome* was used as an exemplar for
such pocket editions of atlases. (Ortelius's *Epitome* is a small atlas, made for people
who could not afford the large atlases.) This map is a direct reduction of the large
map in Mercator's atlas.

Occurrence in atlases
351:01 Atlas Minor, Hondius-Claesz.-Jansz., [1607]: 8 D4r
351:11 Atlas Minor, Hondius-Claesz.-Jansz., 1608: 8 D4r 31
351:21 Atlas Minor, Hondius-Claesz.-Jansz., 1609: 8 E2r 35
351:02 Atlas Minor, Hondius-Claesz.-Jansz., 1610: 8 D4r 31
351:12/13 Atlas Minor, Hondius-Claesz.-Jansz., 1613/14: 8 D4r 31
351:03 Atlas Minor, Jansz., 1620-21: 8 D4r 31
351:31 Historia Mundi or Mercator's Atlas, Cotes, 1635-39: 8 E2r 39(45)

References   Shirley 1991 (Br. Isl. I), 283.

12.1   [5000:352.1] British Isles
ANGLIA | SCOTIA | et | Hibernia.
England, Scotland and Ireland
14 X 20 cm.

Notes   A new edition of Mercator's *Atlas Minor* (see 5100:331) was published by Johannes Janssonius. The plates were engraved by Pieter van den Keere and Abraham Goos. Hondius followed Mercator in his editions, but Janssonius used the maps of John Speed as an exemplar for his maps.

Occurrence in atlases

352:01 Atlas Minor, Janssonius, 1628: 8 D4r 31
352:21 Atlas Minor, Janssonius, 1630: 8 E2 37
352:31 Atlas Minor, Janssonius, 1631: 8 D4r 31
352:02 Atlas Minor, Janssonius, 1634: 8 D4r 31
352:32/33 Atlas Minor, Janssonius, 1648-51: VI 4 B4r 15

References   Shirley 1991 (Br. Isl. I), 401.

12.2   [5000:352.2] **British Isles**
ANGLETERRE | ÉCOSSE | et | IRLANDE.
England, Scotland and Ireland

Notes   This map appeared in the *Atlas soulagé de son gros & pesant fardeau*, published by Pieter van der Aa. Almost all the maps are printed from reworked plates of Janssonius's *Atlas Minor*. The titles and scale were translated into French. Several Latin texts on the maps have been removed, as have the Latin names of the wind directions in the borders. The cartouches have been modernized and windroses added. Other modernizations were the removal of ships and sea monsters, and erasing names in curled letters and replacing them with Roman type letters. Latin names of seas and countries are often translated into French.

Occurrence in atlases
352:51.2-9 Atlas soulagé…, Van der Aa, c. 1714: v4 1 blank

13   [5000:353] **British Isles**
      ANGLIA | SCOTIA | et | HIBERNIA.
      England, Scotland and Ireland
      19 x 26 cm.

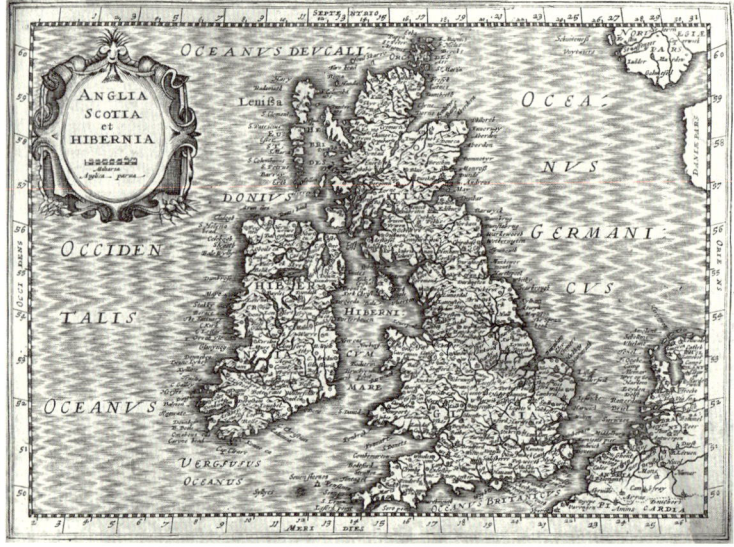

Notes   Jan Cloppenburg published the fourth and final series of reduced versions of Mercator's *Atlas*. The maps were engraved by Pieter van den Keere and are larger then the preceding examples. The sea is engraved with a remarkable zig-zag design.

Occurrence in atlases

353:01/02 Atlas, Evertsz. Cloppenburch, 1630/36: 8 D4r 31
353:11 Atlas, Evertsz. Cloppenburch, 1632: 8 D4r 31
353:21 Atlas, Janssonius van Waesbergen, 1673: 109 blank
353:31 Nieuwe en beknopte Uytbeeldinge en Vertooninge der gantscher Aerdbodem, Janssonius van Waesbergen, 1676: 117 blank
353:41/42 Atlas Portatif..., Du Sauzet, 1734: 189 blank

References   Shirley 1991 (Br. Isl. I), 412.

14   [5000:381] **British Isles**
BRITANICÆ INSVLAE.
British Isles
13 X 17 cm.

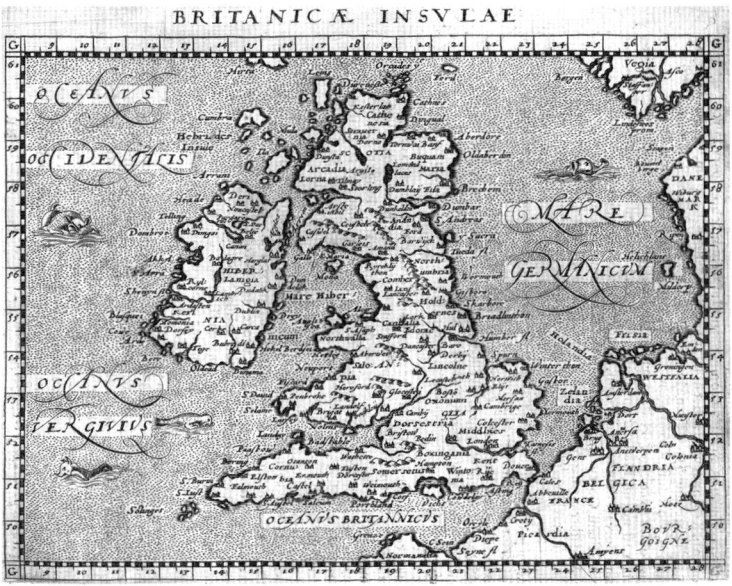

Notes   This is a revised version of a map that appeared in the edition of Ptolemy's 'Geographia' published by Giovanni Magini.

Occurrence in atlases
381:01-03 Geographie Universae, Kesched-Jansz., 1597-1617: 31 E6v 34(39)

References   Shirley 1991 (Br. Isl. I), 197.

15   [5050:342] Great Britain
        Magna | Britannia.
        Great Britain
        10 x 14 cm.

Notes   This map is from Petrus Bertius' *Tabularum Geographicorum Contractarum Libri...*, which followed Barent Langenes' *Caert Thresoor*. Bertius first applied texts for the Langenes atlas, but in 1616 he made his own pocket atlas. Remarkable for its western orientation.

Occurrence in atlases
342:01 Tabulae Geographicae Contractae, Bertius, 1616/18: 22 H2v 116
342:11 La Geographie Racourcie de Pierre Bertius, Hondius jr, 1618: 22 H2v 116
342:21 Atlas Minor, J. Blaeu, 1637: 81

References   Shirley 1991 (Br. Isl. I), 348.

16.1   [5100:1A.1] England
ANGLIA | regnum
The Kingdom of England
Per Gerardum Mercatorem.
35 x 45.5 cm.

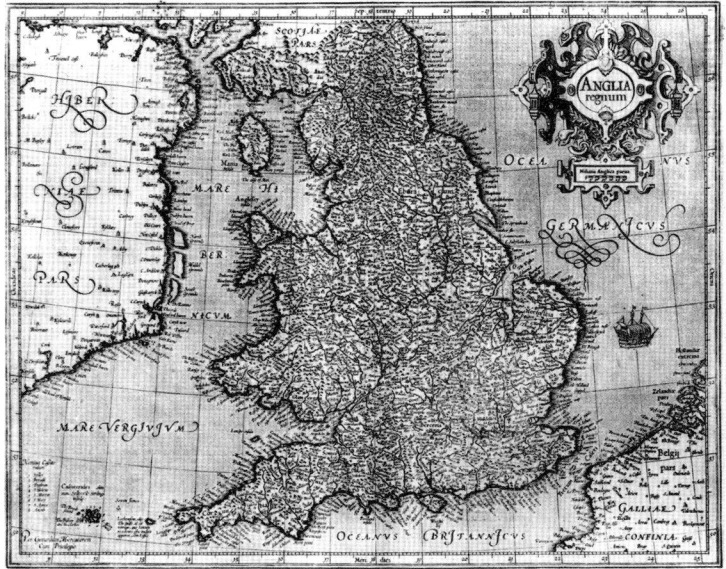

Notes   The maps for the *Atlas* of Gerard Mercator (1512–1594) – the first book with the title atlas – were published in five parts between 1585 and 1595. The fifth part (maps of the British Isles, Northern and Eastern Europe) was prepared for publication by Gerard's son Rumold Mercator in 1595.

Occurrence in atlases   1:011/12 Atlas, Mercator, 1595: 17 XII
1:101 Hondius-Claesz., 1606: 18 X 65-66 MP
1:102 Atlas, Hondius-Claesz., 1607-08: 18 X 63-64
1:111 Atlas, Hondius, 1609: 18 X 63-64
1:103 Atlas, Hondius, 1611-12: 18 X 63-64
1:104 Atlas, Hondius jr, 1613-19: 18 2A 63-64
1:112 Atlas,l Hondius jr, 1613-16: 18 Y 69-70
1:113 Atlas, Hondius jr, 1619: 18 X 63-64
1:105 Atlas, Hondius, 1623: 18 2A 63-64
1:114 Atlas, Hondius, 1628: 18 2G 117-120
1:107 Atlas, Hondius, 1630: 19 2B 65-66
1:311 Atlas, Hondius, 1633: vi 19 2G 117-120
1:321/22 Atlas, Janssonius-Hondius, 1633: 10 K 27-40
1:331 Atlas, Janssonius-Hondius, 1634: 12 M 23-24

References   Shirley 1991, no. 181.

16.2 [5100:1A.2] England
ANGLIA | REGNUM
The Kingdom of England

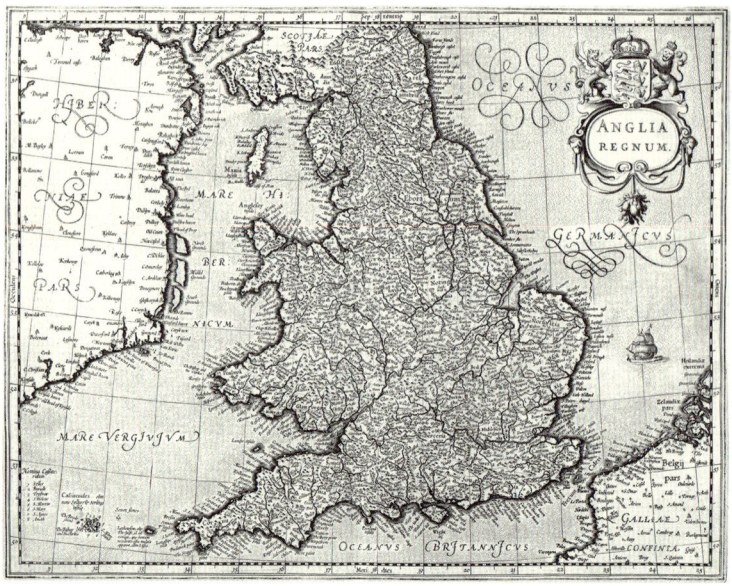

Notes This Mercator map was published in the Hondius/Janssonius atlas of 1636–1641. There is a new title cartouche, Mercator's name is erased and some geographical changes are made.

Occurrence in atlases
1:341 Hondius-Janssonius, 1636-41: VI 6 S 55-56

References Shirley 1991, no. 463.

17   [5100:1B] England
ANGLIA | REGNVM
The Kingdom of England
Amstelodami, | Apud Ioannem Ianßonium
38.5 x 50.5 cm.

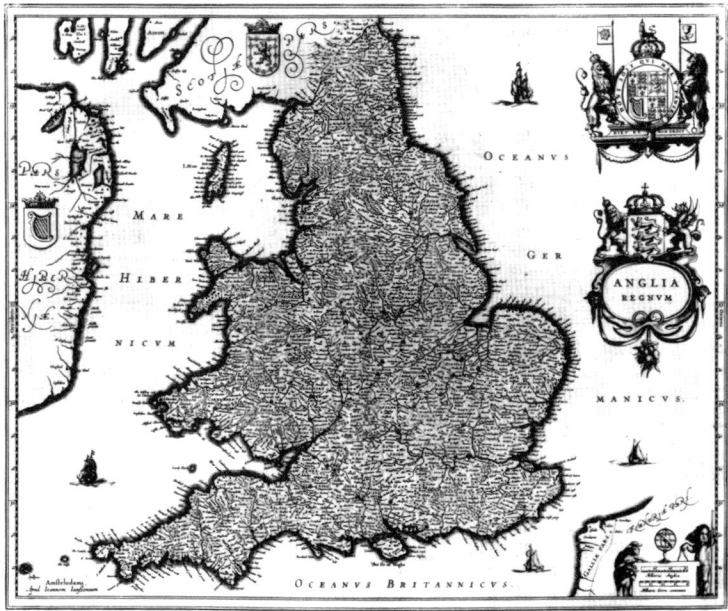

Notes   This Janssonius map closely resembles the Blaeu map, published two
years earlier. Probably Janssonius worked with the Blaeu map as exemplar, instead
of the Speed map, which Blaeu had copied. The coats of arms on the right are of
the royal family (above) and of England.

Occurrence in atlases
1:324 Appendix Atlantis, Janssonius, 1636: 12 L
1:323 Newer Atlas, Janssonius, 1636: VI 18 Q(L)
1:332 Appendix Atlantis, Janssonius/Hondius, 1637: 10 M
1:401 Atlas Novus, Janssonius-Hondius, 1638: VI 18 T
1:421/2 Newer Atlas, Janssonius, 1638: VI 15 L
1:431 Nieuwen Atlas, Janssonius, 1638-44: VI 14 R(M)
1:411/2 Nouveau Theatre du Monde, Hondius, 1639-42: VI 18 R(K)
1:424/27 Atlas Novus, Janssonius, 1644-45: VI 8 I
1:433/36 Nieuwen Atlas, Janssonius, 1638-44/1658: VI 7 G
1:413 Nouveau Theatre du Monde, Janssonius, 1644-47: VI 10 K(R)
1:403/05 Atlas Novus, Janssonius, 1647/1657-62: V4 4 T 67-68
1:414/15 Le Nouvel Atlas... Tome Quatrieme, Janssonius, 1646-49: V4 4 Z
77-78
1:425 Novus Atlas, Janssonius, 1647-49: V4 4 2A 87-88

1:434/36 Nieuwen Atlas... Het Vierde deel, Janssonius, 1647-49/1658: v4 4 2E
1:441 Nuovo Atlas, Janssonius, 1653-66: v4 58 C&D
1:407 Atlas Contractus, Janssonius, 1666: vi 75
1:408 Atlas, Janssonius, after c. 1680: v3 3

References   Shirley 1991, no. 465.

18   [5100:2] **England**
ANGLIA | REGNVM
The Kingdom of England
38.5 x 50 cm.

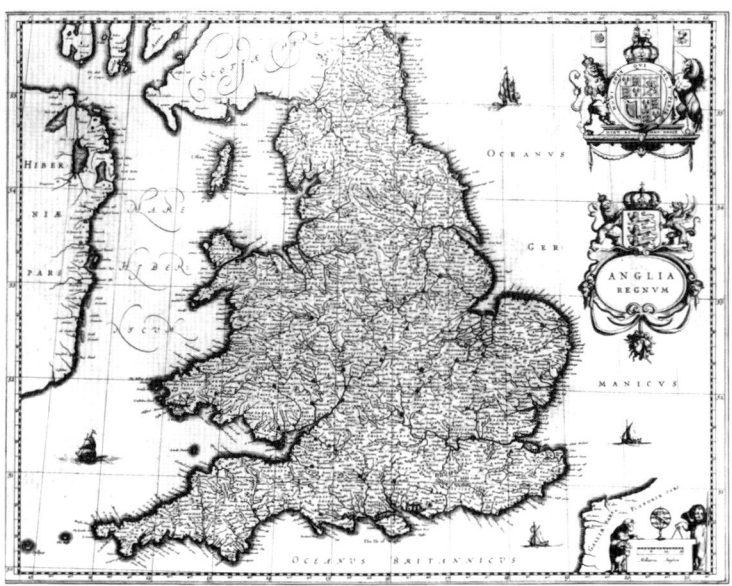

Notes   The map is a copy of Speed's *Theatre* dated 1611 and appears in Blaeu's
atlases from 1635.

Occurrence in atlases

2:131 Novus Atlas, W.J. Blaeu, 1634/35: v1 8 H

2:132 Novus Atlas, W.J. Blaeu, 1635: v1 8 H

2:132 Theatrum Orbis Terrarum, W.& J. Blaeu, 1635: v1 8 L

2:111-12 Le Theatre du Monde, W. & J. Blaeu, 1635: v1 9 L2

2:121 Toonneel des Aerdrycks, W. & J. Blaeu, 1635: v1 102 3A

2:201 Theatrum Orbis Terrarum, W. & J. Blaeu, 1640: v3 64 C 4

2:211 Theatre du Monde ou Nouvel Atlas, J. & C. Blaeu, 1640-43: v3 64 C 3 or 3A

2:221 Toonneel des Aerdrycks, J. & C. Blaeu, 1642-43: v3 64 C 3

2:231 Novus Atlas, J. 7 C. Blaeu, 1641-42: v3 64 B

2:212-3 Theatre du Monde ou Nouvel Atlas, J. Blaeu, 1643-45: v3 64 C 3

2:202-3 Theatrum Orbis Terrarum, J. Blaeu, 1644-45: v3 64 C 4

2:301 Theatrum Orbis Terrarum sive Atlas Novus Pars Quarta, J. Blaeu, 1646: 3
blank

2:302-3 Theatrum Orbis Terrarum sive Atlas Novus Pars Quarta, J. Blaeu, 1646-
48: 3 V 73-74

2:311 Le Theatre du Monde ou Nouvel Atlas, Quatriesme Partie, J. Blaeu: 3
blank

2:312 Cinquème Volume de la Geographie Blaviane, J. Blaeu, 1663-67: 3 R 61-62

2:321 Toonneel des Aerdycks oft Nieuwe Atlas... Vierde deel, J. Blaeu, 1648: 3 Z 81-82

2:322 Toonneel des Aerdycks oft Nieuwe Atlas... Vierde deel, J. Blaeu, 1648: 3 T 69-70

2:331 Novus Atlas and Atlas Major (Vierter Teil), J. Blaeu, 1645-48: 3 blank

2:232 Novus Atlas, J. Blaeu, 1647-49: v3 64 B

Nuevo Atlas del Reyno de Inglaterra, J. Blaeu, 1645/48: 3 Z 81-82

References   Van der Krogt 2002 18:11.

19   [5100:31A] England
ANGLIAE | REGNI FLO- | RENTISSIMI | NOVA DESCRIP- |
TIO
AVCTORE | HVMFREDO | LHVYD DEN | BYGIENSE | [-] | 1573.
A new representation of England, a most flourishing kingdom, by
Humphrey Llwyd from Denbigh
37.5 x 46.5 cm.

Notes   The sources for this map were Mercator's wall map of the British Isles,
1564, and a manuscript map by Humphrey Llwyd from 1568.

Occurrence in atlases
31:290 Theatrum Orbis Terrarum, Koler, 1572: 8 (1575)
31:110/111 Theatre oft Toonneel des Aerdtbodems, Coppens van Diest, 1571/73:
2 #6B
31:210 Ein Zusatz bei dass Theatrum, [Coppens van Diest], 1573: 2 #6B
31:010 Additamentum Theatri Orbis Terrarum, [Coppens van Diest], 1573: 2 #6B
31:310 Addition de Théatre de l'Universe, [Coppens van Diest], 1573: 2 #6B
31:011 Theatrum Orbis Terrarum, Coppens van Diest, 1573: 8 #8
31:211 Theatrum oder Schawbüch der Ertkreijs, Plantin, 1580: 8 #6B
31:012 Theatrum Orbis Terrarum, Coppens van Diest, 1574: 8 #8
31:311 Théatre de l'Univers, Coppens van Diest, 1574/72: 8 #6B
31:013 Theatrum Orbis Terrarum,Van den Rade, 1575: 8 #8
31:021-022 Theatrum Orbis Terrarum, Plantin, 1579: 10 #10
31:211/022 Theatrum oder Schawbüch der Ertkreijs, Plantin, 1580: 10 #10
31:321 Théatre de l'Univers, Plantin, 1581: 10 #10

31:031 Theatrum Orbis Terrarum, Plantin, 1584: 11 #11
31:331 Théatre de l'Univers, Plantin, 1587: 11 #11
31:431 Theatro de la Tierra Universal, Plantin, 1588: 11 #11
31:041 Theatrum Orbis Terrarum, Plantin, 1592: 12 #12
31:051 Theatrum Orbis Terrarum, Plantin, 1595: 12 #12
31:051 Theatrum Orbis Terrarum, [Claesz.], 1598: 11 #11
31:351 Théatre de l'Univers, Plantin, 1598: 12 #12
31:041 Theatrum Orbis Terrarum,Moretus, 1601: 12 #12
31:451 Theatro d'el Orbe de la Tierra, Vrients, 160212 #12
31:251 Theatrum oder Schawbuch der gantzen Welt, Vrients, 1602: 12 #12
31:551 The Theatre of the Whole World, Norton, 1606: 158 {xlij}
31:452-454 Theatro d'el Orbe de la Tierra, Vrienst, 1602/1609[1641]): 12 #12

References Van den Broecke 2011, 19; Karrow 1993, 1/79; Meurer 1991, 55; Shirley 1991 (Br. Isl. I), 98.

20   [5100:31B] England
        ANGLIA, | REGNUM | Si quod aliud in | toto Oceano ditis- | simum
        et flo- | rentissimum
        Christo- | phorus | Saxton | descri- | bebat | 1579.
        The kingdom of England, entirely located in the ocean as it is, very
        rich and flourishing
        38.5 x 48 cm.

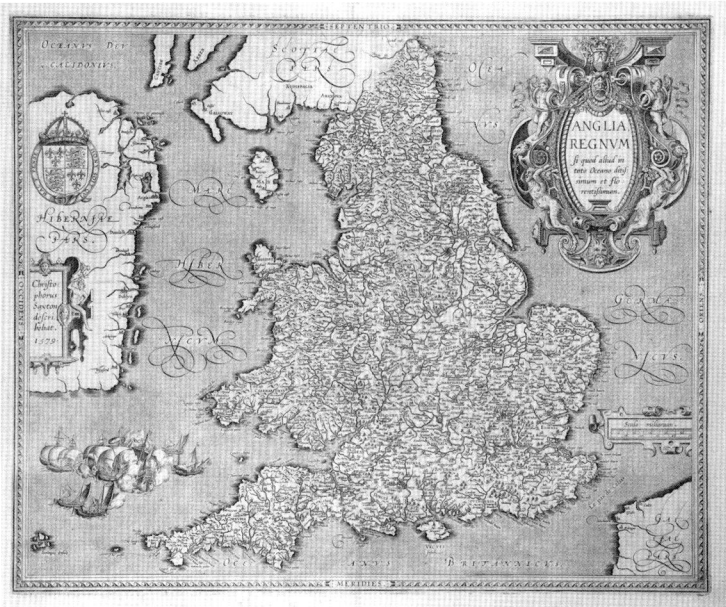

Notes   The sources for this map can be found in the atlas of Christopher Saxton
published in 1579.

Occurrence in atlases
31:451 Theatro d'el Orbe de la Tierra, Vrients, 1602 12 #12
31:041 Theatrum Orbis Terrarum, Vrients, 1603: 12 #12
31:452-454 Theatro d'el Orbe de la Tierra, Vrienst, 1602/1609[1641]): 12 #12
31:122 Theatrum Orbis Terrarum, Vrients, 1598, J. Moretus, 1598: 11 #11

References   Van den Broecke 2011, 20; Meurer 1991, 143; Shirley 1991 (Br. Isl. I), 258.

21 [5100:331] **England**
[Map of England].
8 x 11 cm.

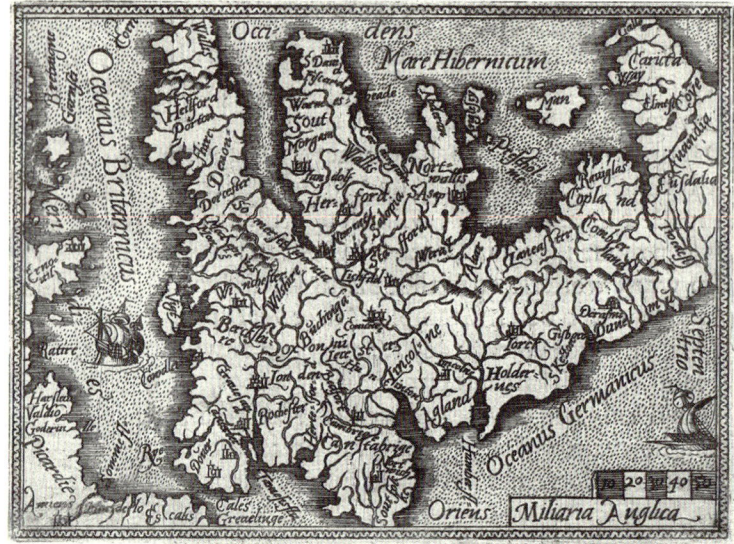

Notes This map was first published in the *Spiegel der Werelt* by Pieter Heyns, a small atlas containing texts in rhyme. The outlines of the map are based on the work of Mercator, which was published in Ortelius's atlases.

Occurrence in atlases
331:01 Spieghel der Werelt, Heyns, 1577: 6 D1r 7
331:11 Le Miroir du Monde, Heyns, 1579: 6 B1r 7
331:02/03 Spieghel der Werelt, Heyns, 1583/96: 6 D1r 7
331:12 Le Miroir du Monde, Heyns, 1583: 6 C1r 7
331:21 Theatri Orbis Terrarum Enchiridion, Favolli, 1585: 6 B3v 10
332:01/02 Epitome du Théatre du Monde, Galle, 1588/90: 6 A6r 6
332:11 Epitome Theatri Orteliani, Galle, 1598: 6 B6r 6
332:21 Theatro d'Abrahamo Ortelio, Galle, 1593: 6 B5r 5

References Shirley 1991 (Br. Isl. I), 118.

22   [5100:332] England
ANGLIA.
England
7.5 x 10.5 cm.

Notes   This map replaced map 5100:331 in the new edition of Ortelius' *Epitome*,
a small atlas, made for people who could not afford the large atlases.

Occurrence in atlases
332:21 Theatro d'Abrahamo Ortelio, Galle, 1593: 6 B5r 5
332:12 Epitome Theatri Orteliani, Galle, 1595: 6 B6r 6
332:03 Epitome du Théatre du Monde, Galle, 1598: 6 A6r 6
332:13 Epitome Theatri Orteliani, Vrients, 1601: 9 B6r 6
332:22 Breve Compendio dal Theatro Orteliano, Vrients, 1602: 9 B5r 5
332:04 Abrégé du Théatre d'Ortelius, Vrients, 1602: 9 A6r 6
332:31 An Epitome of Ortelius his Theatre, Norton, [1602]: 8 B6r 6

References   Shirley 1991 (Br. Isl. I), 187.

23   [5100:333] England
ANGLIA.
England
8.5 X 12.5 cm.

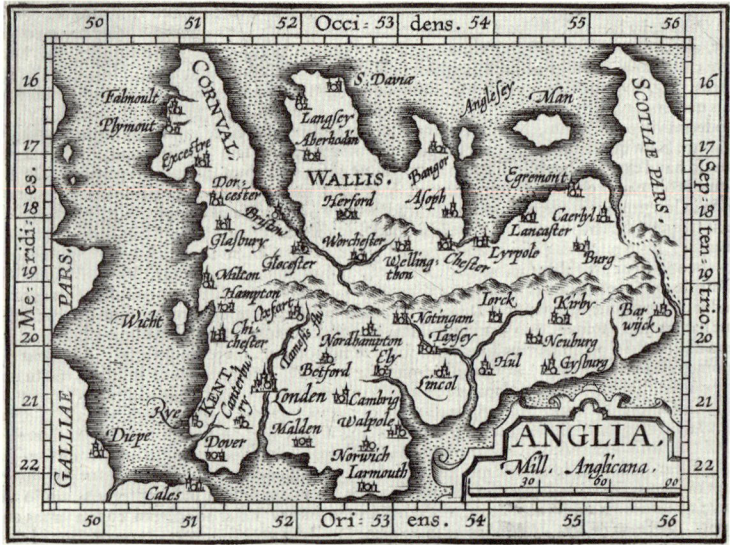

Notes This is another map from Ortelius's *Epitome* (see also 5100:331 and 5100:332). In this map a graticule was added and the title cartouche was made more decorative. The map was engraved by the Aertsen brothers, Ambrosius and Ferdinand, for Johannes van Keerbergen.

Occurrence in atlases
333:01 Epitome Theatri Orbis Terrarum, Van Keerbergen, 1601: 6 A6r 6
333:11 L'Epitome du Théatre de l'Univers, Van Keerbergen, 1602: 6 A6r 6
333:21/22 Breve Compendio dal Theatro Orteliano, Vrients, 1602/1612: 9 B5r 5
333:31 Epitome of the Theatre of the Worlde, Shawe, 1603: 6 A6r 6
333:41 Außzug auß des Abrahami Ortely Theatro Orbis, Hulsius, 1604: 56 L11r 56
(only one copy consulted)

References Shirley 1991 (Br. Isl. I), 236.

24   [5100:333B] England
ANGLIÆ | REGNVM.
Kingdom of England.
9 X 12.5 cm.

Notes   This map of England appeared only in the 1609 edition of the Epitome published by Jan Baptiste Vrients.

Occurrence in atlases
333:02/03 Epitome Theatri Orbis Terrarum, Vrients, 1609/Plantin, 1612: 9C1r6

25   [5100:341] England
ANGLIA
England
Pe. Kærius fecit.
8.5 x 12.5 cm.

Notes   The second state (1599) has graduation and latitude numerals added at the upper and lower borders. The third state (1649) has the engraved reference a.10 added.

Occurrence in atlases

341:01 Caert-Thresoor, Langenes, 1598: 8 C6r 43

341:02 Caert-Thresoor,Claesz, 1599: 8 C6r 43

341:11 Thrésor de Chartes, Claesz., c. 1600: 8 D1r 49

341:51 Tabulae Geographicae Contractae, Bertius, 1600: 8 D5r 57

341:52 Tabulae Geographicae Contractae Editio Secunda, Bertius, 1602/038 D7v 62

341:12/13 Thrésor de Chartes, Claesz., 1602 / Laurensz., 1609: 8 D1r 49

341:53 Tabulae Geographicae Contractae Editio Tertia, Bertius, 1606: 8 D7v 62

341:03 Hand-boeck of Cort Begrijp der Caerten, Claesz., 1609: 8 C8r 47

341:61/62 (1612/50 Tabeln): 7 E8r 79

341:54 Tabulae Geographicae Contractae, C.J. Visscher, 1649: 9 a.10

References   Shirley 1991 (Br. Isl. I), 203 and 219 (variant).

26   [5100:342] England
ANGLIA
England
S. Rogiers Cælavit.
9.5 x 13.5 cm.

Notes   This map of England is from Petrus Bertius' *Tabularum Geographicorum Contractarum Libri ...*, which followed Barent Langenes' *Caert Thresoor*. Bertius first applied texts for the Langenes atlas, but in 1616 he made his own pocket atlas.

Occurrence in atlases
342:01 Tabulae Geographicae Contractae, Bertius, 1616/18: 26 I2v 132
342:11 La Geographie Racourcie de Pierre Bertius, Hondius jr, 1618: 26 I2v 132
342:21 Atlas Minor, J. Blaeu, 1637: 85

References   Shirley 1991 (Br. Isl. I), 349.

27   [5100:351] England
ANGLIA.
England
14 X 18.5 cm.

Notes   A map of England and Wales, which was reduced in size from a map in the large atlas by Mercator. This map was one of the seventeen maps devoted to the British Isles in the Hondius pocket atlas (*Atlas Minor*), dated 1607.

Occurrence in atlases

351:01 Atlas Minor, Hondius-Claesz.-Jansz., [1607]: 17 I2r
351:11 Atlas Minor, Hondius-Claesz.-Jansz., 1608 [Fr.]): 17 I2r 67
351:21 Atlas Minor, Hondius-Claesz.-Jansz., 1609: 17 K2r 75
351:02 Atlas Minor, Hondius-Claesz.-Jansz., 1610: 17 I2r 67
351:12/13 Atlas Minor, Hondius-Claesz.-Jansz., 1613/14: 17 I2r 67
351:03 Atlas Minor, Jansz., 1620-21: 17 I2r 67
351:31 Historia Mundi or Mercator's Atlas, Cotes, 1635-39: 17 I1r 85

References   Shirley 1991 (Br. Isl. I), 284.

28.1   [5100:352.1] England
        ANGLIA.
        England
        14 X 19.5 cm.

Notes   A new edition of Mercator's *Atlas Minor* (see 5100:331) was published by Johannes Janssonius. The plates were engraved by Piter van den Keere and Abraham Goos. Hondius followed Mercator in his editions, but Janssonius used the maps of John Speed as an exemplar for his maps.

Occurrence in atlases
352:01 Atlas Minor, Janssonius, 1628: 15 H2r 59
352:11 Atlas Minor, Janssonius, 1630: 15 I4 71
352:31 Atlas Minor, Janssonius, 1631: 15 H2r 59
352:02 Atlas Minor, Janssonius, 1634: 15 H2r 59
352:32/33 Atlas Minor, Janssonius, 1648-51: vi 5 C2r 19

References   Shirley 1991 (Br. Isl. I), 402.

28.2   [5100:352.2] England
L'ANGLE- | TERRE.
England

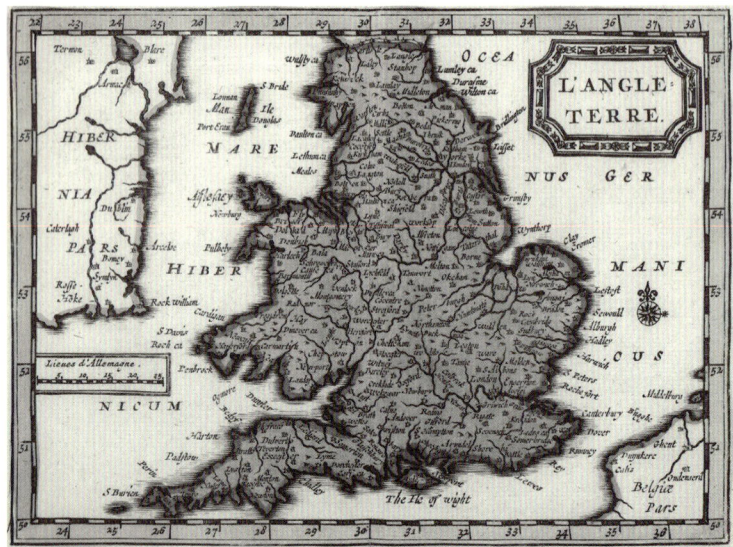

Notes   This map appeared in the *Nouveau Petit Atlas*, published by Pieter van der Aa. Almost all the maps are printed from reworked plates of Janssonius's *Atlas Minor*. The titles and scale were translated into French. Several Latin texts on the maps have been removed, as have the Latin names of the wind directions in the borders. The cartouches have been modernized and windroses added. Other modernizations are the removal of ships and sea monsters, and erasing names in curled letters and replacing them with Roman type letters. Latin names of seas and countries are often translated into French.

Occurrence in atlases
352:51.1 Nouveau Petit Atlas, Van der Aa, c. 1714: 27 blank
352:51.2-9 Atlas soulagé..., Van der Aa, c. 1714: v4 2 blank

29.1   [5100:353.1] England
ANGLIAE | REGNUM.
The Kingdom of England
19 x 26 cm.

Notes   Jan Cloppenburg published the fourth and final series of reduced versions of Mercator's *Atlas*. The maps were engraved by Pieter van den Keere and are larger than the preceding examples. The sea is engraved with a remarkable zig-zag design.

Occurrence in atlases

353:01/02 Atlas, Evertsz. Cloppenburch, 1630/36: 17 I2r 67(65)
353:11 Atlas, Evertsz. Cloppenburch, 1632: 17 I2r 67
353:21 Atlas, Janssonius van Waesbergen, 1673: 110 blank
353:31 Nieuwe en beknopte Uytbeeldinge en Vertooninge der gantscher Aerdbodem, Janssonius van Waesbergen, 1676: 118 blank

References   Shirley 1991 (Br. Isl. I), 413.

29.2   [5100:353.2] England
       L'ANGLETERRE.
       England

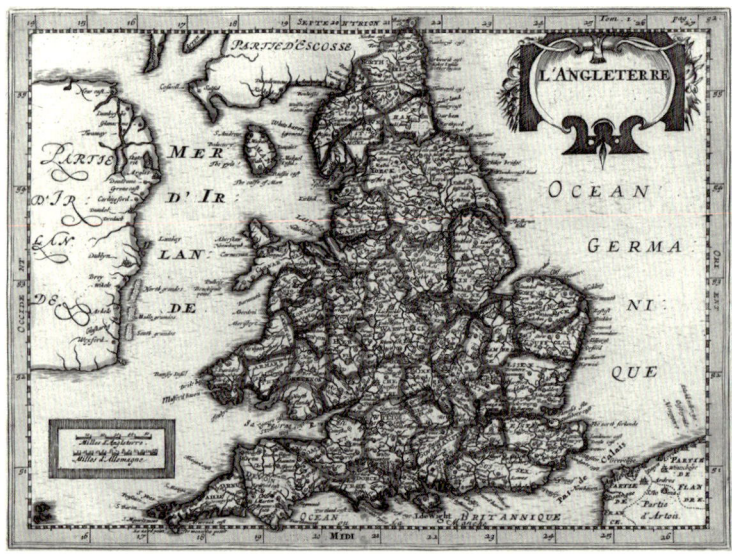

Notes   This map appeared in the *Atlas portatif composé de CCLXXXV cartes* by Henri du Sauzet. This is basically a new edition of the Cloppenburch atlas. Many of the plates are reworked, several just by adding some ships in the seas, others by adding a new title and scale bar in French.

Occurrence in atlases
353:41/42 Atlas Portatif..., Du Sauzet, 1734: 190 blank

30.1   [5110:1.1] England (North)
NORTH- | VMBRIA, CVM- | BERLANDIA, ET | DVNELMEN-
SIS | Episcopa- | tus
Northumberland, Cumberland and the diocese of Durham
Per Gerardum Mercatorem.
35 x 46.5 cm.

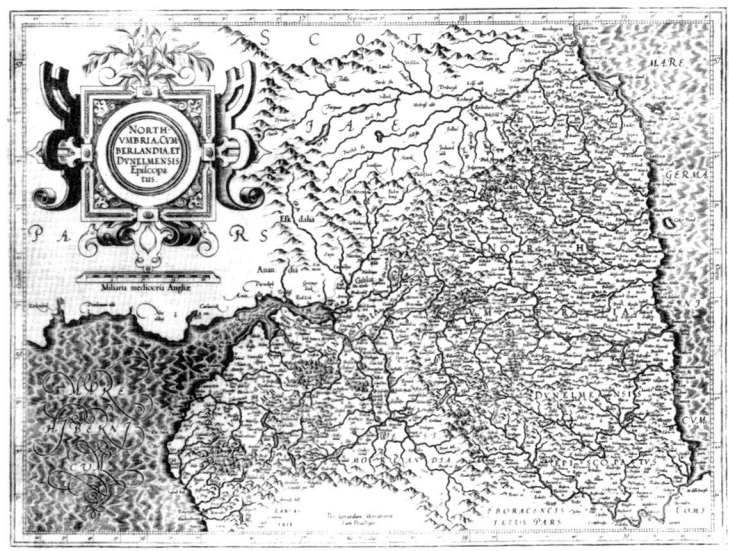

Notes   The maps for the *Atlas* of Gerard Mercator (1512-1594) – the first book
with the title atlas – were published in five parts between 1585 and 1595. The fifth
part (maps of the British Isles, Northern and Eastern Europe) was prepared for
publication by Gerard's son Rumold Mercator in 1595 and lacks a title page.

Occurrence in atlases   1:011/12 Atlas, Mercator, 1595: 18 XIII
1:101 Hondius-Claesz., 1606: 19 Y 67-68
1:102 Atlas, Hondius-Claesz., 1607-08: 19 Y 65-66
1:111 Atlas, Hondius, 1609: 19 Y 65-66
1:103 Atlas, Hondius, 1611-12: 19 Y 65-66
1:104 Atlas, Hondius jr, 1613-19: 19 2B 65-66
1:112 Atlas,l Hondius jr, 1613-16: 19 Z 71-72
1:113 Atlas, Hondius jr, 1619: 19 Y 65-66
1:105 Atlas, Hondius, 1623: 19 2B 65-66
1:114 Atlas, Hondius, 1628: 19 2H 121-124
1:107 Atlas, Hondius, 1630: 20 2C 67-68
1:311 Atlas, Hondius, 1633: vi 20 2H 121-124
1:321/22 Atlas, Janssonius-Hondius, 1633: 11 L 41-44
1:331 Atlas, Janssonius-Hondius, 1634: 13 N 25-26

30.2 **[5110:1.2] England (North)**
NORTHUMBRIA, | CUMBERLANDIA, | ET DUNELMENSIS |
EPISCOPATUS
Northumberland, Cumberland and the diocese of Durham
Amstelodami | Sumptibus Henrici Hondij

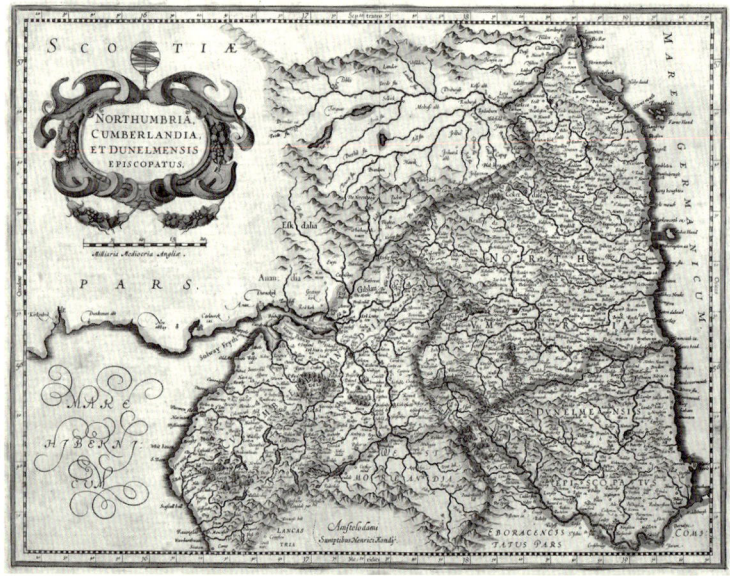

Notes This map first appeared in the first English edition of the Mercator atlas by Hondius and Janssonius. Mercator's plates of the maps of England have been corrected and improved with new vignettes. The name of Mercator was effaced on some, the name of Henricus Hondius added on others.

Occurrence in atlases
1:341 Hondius-Janssonius, 1636-41: VI 7 T 57-58
1:401 Atlas Novus, Janssonius-Hondius, 1638: VI 19 V
1:411/2 Nouveau Theatre du Monde, Hondius, 1639-42: VI 19 S

31   [5110:342] **England (North)**
Northumbr. | Cumberlan. | Dunelm. Episcop.
Northumberland, Cumberland and the diocese of Durham
9.5 x 13.5 cm.

Notes   This map is one of a new series of engraved plates which were made for the editions of Bertius's *Tabulae Geographicae Contractae*, to be published by Jodocus Hondius junior. The plates were used to illustrate some other books with maps, such as Paullus Merula's *Cosmographia Generalis*, printed in Leiden by Isaac Elsevier for Jodocus Hondius junior.

Occurrence in atlases
342:01 Tabulae Geographicae Contractae, Bertius, 1616/18: 27 I5v 138
342:11 La Geographie Racourcie de Pierre Bertius, Hondius jr, 1618: 27 I5v 138
342:21 Atlas Minor, J. Blaeu, 1637: 86

32   [5110:351] England (North)
Northumbr. | Cumberla<u>n</u>dia | Dunelm. Episcop.
Northumberland, Cumberland and the diocese of Durham
13.5 X 19 cm.

Notes   The first appearance of this map in an atlas is in the *Atlas Minor* published
by Hondius, Cornelis Claesz. and Jan Jansz. The first mention of this atlas is in the
'Const ende caert-register', the 1609 map catalogue by Cornelis Claesz., as 'Atlas
Minor Gerardi Mercatoris à I. Hondio [...] Illustratus in 4o. Amsterodami apud
Cornelium Nicolai, 1608'.

Occurrence in atlases

351:01 Atlas Minor, Hondius-Claesz.-Jansz., [1607]: 18 I4r
351:11 Atlas Minor, Hondius-Claesz.-Jansz., 1608 [Fr.]): 18 I4r 71
351:21 Atlas Minor, Hondius-Claesz.-Jansz., 1609: 18 L1r 81
351:02 Atlas Minor, Hondius-Claesz.-Jansz., 1610: 18 I4r 71
351:12/13 Atlas Minor, Hondius-Claesz.-Jansz., 1613/14: 18 I4r 71
351:03 Atlas Minor, Jansz., 1620-21: 18 I4r 71
351:31 Historia Mundi or Mercator's Atlas, Cotes, 1635-39: 18 I3r 89

33.1   [5110:352.1] England (North)
Northumbria, | Cumberlandia, Dunelmensis episc. | Westmorlandia,
et Mania Ins.
Northumbria, Cumberland, the diocese of Durham, Westmorland
and the Isle of Man
14 X 19.5 cm.

Notes   Between 1621 and 1625 the copperplates of the *Atlas Minor* were sold to
parties in England. Therefore, Johannes Janssonius, who wanted to publish a new
edition of the *Atlas Minor*, had the engraver Pieter van den Keere make a new set
of copperplates. The first edition of this new *Atlas Minor* was published in 1628.

Occurrence in atlases
352:01 Atlas Minor, Janssonius, 1628: 16 H4r 63
352:11 Atlas Minor, Janssonius, 1630: 16 K3 77
352:31 Atlas Minor, Janssonius, 1631: 16 I1r 65
352:02 Atlas Minor, Janssonius, 1634: 16 H4r 63
352:32/33 Atlas Minor, Janssonius, 1648-51: vi 6 C4r 23

33.2 [5110:352.2] England (North)
Carte de | NORTHUMBERLAND, | DURHAM, CUMBER-
LAND, | WESTMORLAND, | et l'Isle de MAN.
Map of Northumberland, Durham, Cumberland, Westmorland and
the Isle of Man

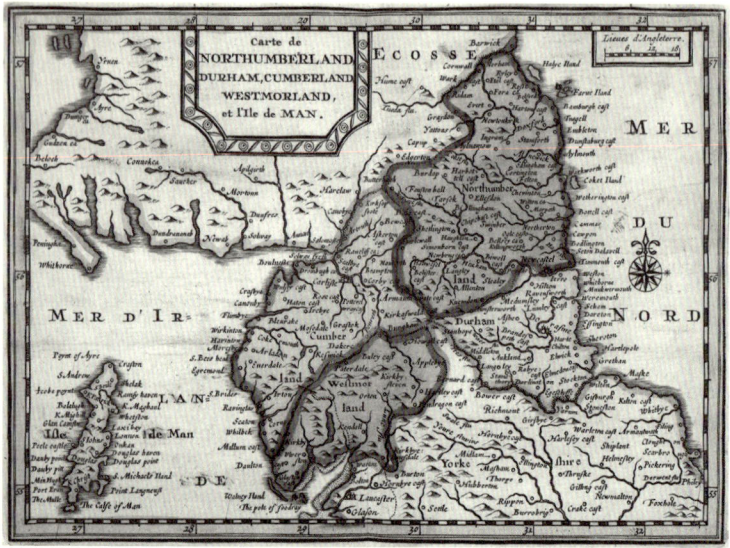

Notes This map appeared in the *Atlas soulagé de son gros & pesant fardeau*, published by Pieter van der Aa. Almost all the maps are printed from reworked plates
of Janssonius's *Atlas Minor*. The titles and scale were translated into French. Several Latin texts on the maps have been removed, as have the Latin names of the
wind directions in the borders. The cartouches have been modernized and windroses added. Other modernizations are the removal of ships and sea monsters,
and erasing names in curled letters and replacing them with Roman type letters.
Latin names of seas and countries are often translated into French.

Occurrence in atlases
352:51.2-9 Atlas soulagé..., Van der Aa, c. 1714: v4 16 blank

34   **[5110:353] England (North)**
NORTH- | VMBRIA, CVM | BERLANDIA ET | DVNELMENSIS | Episcopa- | tus
Northumberland, Cumberland and the diocese of Durham
Petrus Kærius Cælavit.
19 X 25.5 cm.

Notes This map appeared in the *Atlas* of Jan Evertsz. Cloppenburch. This new edition of Mercator's atlas was a competitive one. Its newly engraved maps were of a size that fell in between the folio maps in the Mercator-Hondius atlas and the *Atlas Minor*. Most of the maps were engraved by Pieter van den Keere. Cloppenburch's *Atlas* is dedicated to the States General of the United Provinces and Prince Frederik Hendrik of Orange (1584–1647), *stadhouder* of Holland.

Occurrence in atlases
353:01/02 Atlas, Evertsz. Cloppenburch, 1630/36: 18 I4r 71
353:11 Atlas, Evertsz. Cloppenburch, 1632: 18 I4r 71
353:21 Atlas, Janssonius van Waesbergen, 1673: 115 blank
353:31 Nieuwe en beknopte Uytbeeldinge en Vertooninge der gantscher Aerdbodem, Janssonius van Waesbergen, 1676: 123 blank

35.1 [5111:1.1] England (Northwest) and North Wales
      WEST- | MORLANDIA, LAN- | CASTRIA, CESTRIA, | CAER-
      NARVAN, DENBIGH, | FLINT, MERIONIDH, | MONT-
      GOMERY, SA- | LOPIA | Cum insulis | MANIA ET AN- | GLESEY
      Westmorland, Lancashire, Cheshire, Caernarvon, Denbigh, Flint,
      Merionshire, Montgomery, Shropshire, with the Isles of Man and
      Anglesey
      Per Gerardum Mercatorem.
      36 x 41 cm.

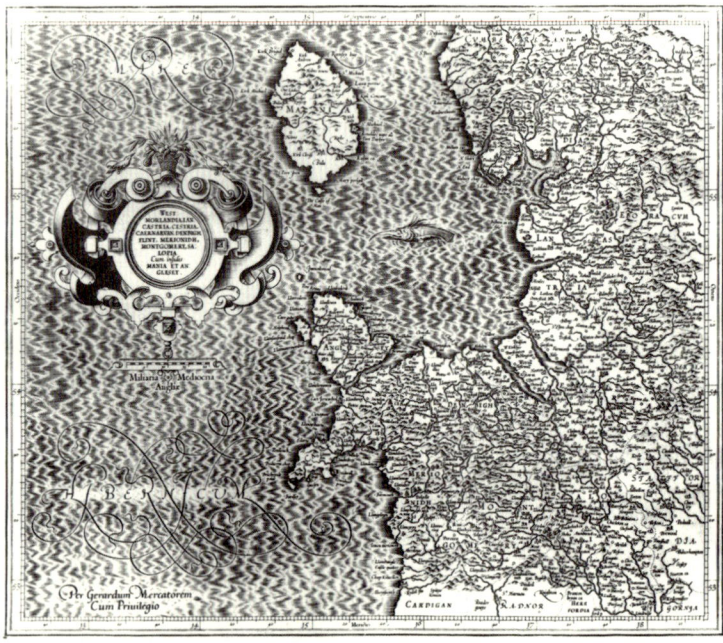

Notes   This map was first published in the 1595 edition of Mercator's *Atlas*,
which was published by his heirs, after Mercator's death in 1594. The map appears
in atlases until 1634.

Occurrence in atlases

1:011/12 Atlas, Mercator, 1595: 19 XIV
1:101 Hondius-Claesz., 1606: 20 Z 69-70
1:102 Atlas, Hondius-Claesz., 1607-08: 20 Z 67-68
1:111 Atlas, Hondius, 1609: 20 Z 67-68
1:103 Atlas, Hondius, 1611-12: 20 Z 67-68
1:104 Atlas, Hondius jr, 1613-19: 20 2C 67-68
1:112 Atlas,l Hondius jr, 1613-16: 20 2A 73-74
1:113 Atlas, Hondius jr, 1619: 20 Z 67-68
1:105 Atlas, Hondius, 1623: 20 2C 67-68
1:114 Atlas, Hondius, 1628: 20 2I 125-128

1:107 Atlas, Hondius, 1630: 21 2D 69-70
1:311 Atlas, Hondius, 1633: VI 21 2I 125-128
1:321/22 Atlas, Janssonius-Hondius, 1633: 12 M 45-48
1:331 Atlas, Janssonius-Hondius, 1634: 14 O 27-28

35.2   [5111:1.2] **England (Northwest) and North Wales**
Westmorlandia | Lancastria, Cestria, | Caernarvan, Denbigh, | Flint,
Merionidh, | Montgomery, Salo- | pia, cum insulis | Mania et An- |
glesey
Westmorland, Lancashire, Cheshire, Caernarvon, Denbigh, Flint,
Merionshire, Montgomery, Shropshire, with the Isles of Man and
Anglesey

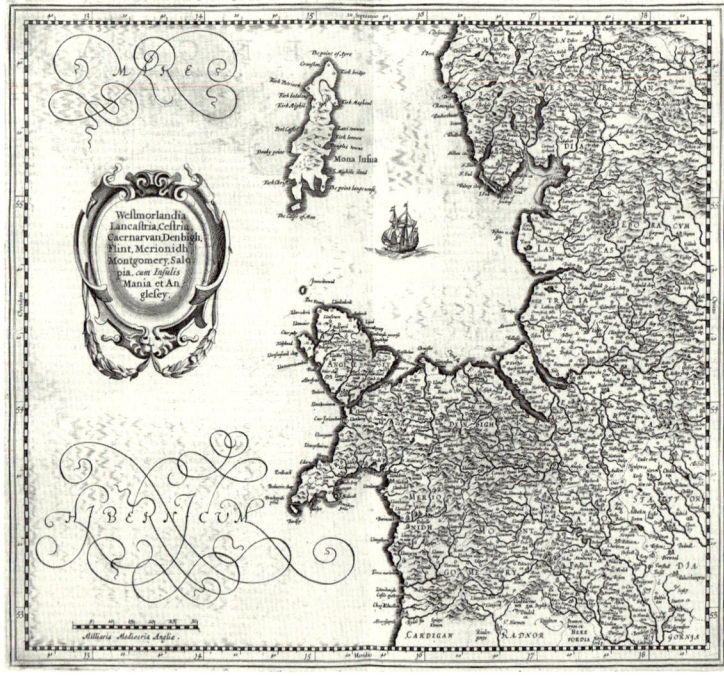

Notes   This map first appeared in the first English edition of the Mercator atlas
by Hondius and Janssonius. Mercator's plates of the maps of England have been
corrected and improved with new vignettes. The name of Mercator was effaced
on some, the name of Henricus Hondius added on others.

Occurrence in atlases
1:341 Hondius-Janssonius, 1636-41: VI 8 V 59-60
1:401 Atlas Novus, Janssonius-Hondius, 1638: VI 20 X
1:411/2 Nouveau Theatre du Monde, Hondius, 1639-42: VI 20 T

36   [5111:342] **England (Northwest)**
Westmorland. | Lancastria | Cestria etc.
Westmorland, Lancashire, Cheshire, etc.
9.5 x 13.5 cm.

Notes   This map is one of a new series of engraved plates which were made for the editions of Bertius's *Tabulae Geographicae Contractae* to be published by Jodocus Hondius junior. The plates were used to illustrate some other books with maps, such as Paullus Merula's *Cosmographia Generalis*, printed in Leiden by Isaac Elsevier for Jodocus Hondius junior.

Occurrence in atlases

342:01 Tabulae Geographicae Contractae, Bertius, 1616/18: 28 I6v 140
342:11 La Geographie Racourcie de Pierre Bertius, Hondius jr, 1618: 28 I6v 140
342:21 Atlas Minor, J. Blaeu, 1637: 87

37   [5111:351] England (Northwest)
WEST- | MORLAND, | CASTRIA, | CESTRIA | etc.
Westmorland, Lancashire, Cheshire, etc.
13.5 x 18 cm.

Notes   In 1607, a year after publishing Mercator's atlas in folio, Hondius published it in a reduced edition, the *Atlas Minor*. In so doing, he followed a tradi-
tion that had begun in Antwerp in 1577 with the *Epitome*, a reduced version of
Ortelius's *Theatrum Orbis Terrarum*.

Occurrence in atlases
351:01 Atlas Minor, Hondius-Claesz.-Jansz., [1607]: 19 K2r
351:11 Atlas Minor, Hondius-Claesz.-Jansz., 1608 [Fr.]): 19 K2r 75
351:21 Atlas Minor, Hondius-Claesz.-Jansz.: 19 L3r 85
351:02 Atlas Minor, Hondius-Claesz.-Jansz., 1610: 19 K2r 75
351:12/13 Atlas Minor, Hondius-Claesz.-Jansz., 1613/14: 19 K2r 75
351:03 Atlas Minor, Jansz., 1620-21: 19 K2r 75
351:31 Historia Mundi or Mercator's Atlas, Cotes, 1635-39: 19 I5r 93

38.1 [5111:352.1] **England (Northwest)**
Lancastria, Cestria, | Caernarvan, Denbich, Flint, | Merionidh, Mont-
gomery, Salopia, | Cardigan, Radnor, Wigornia, et | Ins. Anglesey.
Lancashire, Cheshire, Caernarvon, Denbigh, Flint, Merionshire,
Montgomery, Shropshire, Cardigan, Radnor, Wigornshire and the
Isle of Anglesey
14.5 x 20 cm.

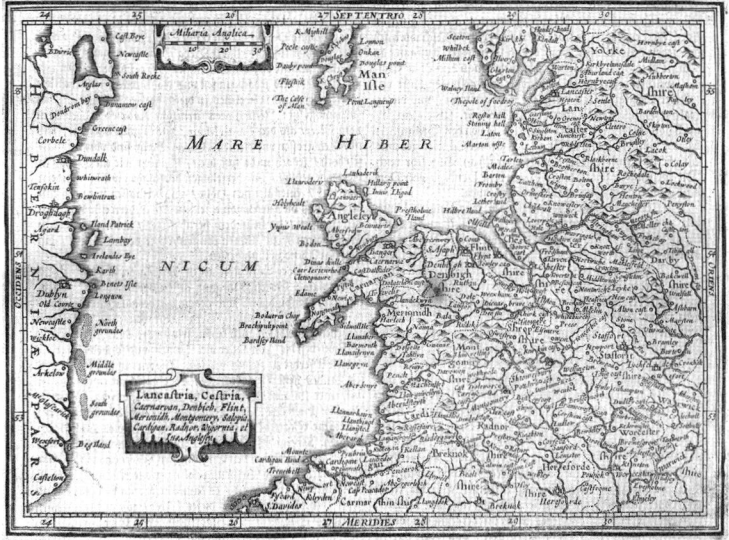

Notes   Between 1621 and 1625 the copperplates of the *Atlas Minor* were sold to
parties in England. Therefore, Johannes Janssonius, who wanted to publish a new
edition of the *Atlas Minor*, had the engraver Pieter van den Keere make a new set
of copperplates. The first edition of this new *Atlas Minor* was published in 1628.

Occurrence in atlases
352:01 Atlas Minor, Janssonius, 1628: 17 I2r 67
352:11 Atlas Minor, Janssonius, 1630: 17 L1 81
352:31 Atlas Minor, Janssonius, 1631: 17 I3r 69
352:02 Atlas Minor, Janssonius, 1634: 17 I2r 67
352:32/33 Atlas Minor, Janssonius, 1648-51: VI 10 E4r 39

38.2   [5111:352.2] England (Northwest)
        Les Comtés de | SHROPS, LANCASTRE, CHESTER | CARDI-
        GAN, RADNOR, | MONTGOMERY, MERIONETH,| CAER-
        NARVAN, DENBIGH, FLINT | et autres.
        Shropshire, Lancashire, Cheshire, Cardigan, Radnor, Montgomery,
        Merionethshire, Caernavon, Denbigh, Flint and others

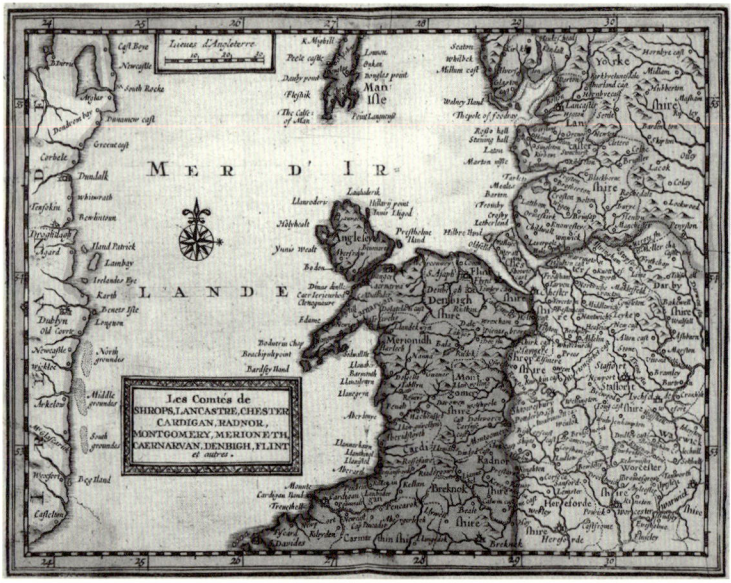

Notes   This map appeared in the *Atlas soulagé de son gros & pesant fardeau*, published by Pieter van der Aa. Almost all the maps are printed from reworked plates
of Janssonius's *Atlas Minor*. The titles and scale were translated into French. Several Latin texts on the maps have been removed, as have the Latin names of the
wind directions in the borders. The cartouches have been modernized and windroses added. Other modernizations are the removal of ships and sea monsters,
and erasing names in curled letters and replacing them with Roman type letters.
Latin names of seas and countries are often translated into French.

Occurrence in atlases
352:51.2-9 Atlas soulagé..., Van der Aa, c. 1714: v4 12 blank

39   [5111:353] England (Northwest)
WESTMORLANDIA, | LANCASTRIA, CESTRIA, | CAER-
NARVAN, DENBIGH, FLINt, | MERIONIDH, MONTGOMERY,
SA- | LOPIA | Cum insulis | MANIA, et ANGLESEY.
Westmorland, Lancashire, Cheshire, Caernarvon, Denbigh, Flint,
Merionshire, Montgomery, Shropshire, with the Isles of Man and
Anglesey
19 X 26 cm.

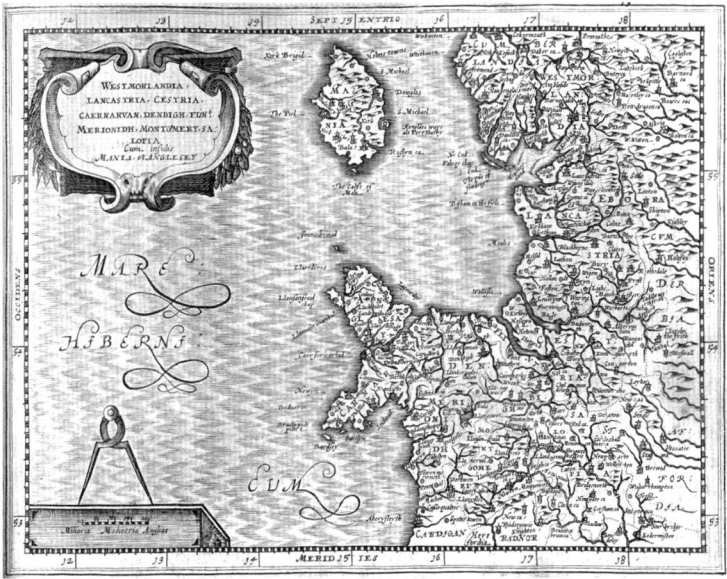

Notes   This map appeared in the *Atlas* of Jan Evertsz. Cloppenburch. This new
edition of Mercator's atlas was a competitive one. Its newly engraved maps were
of a size that fell in between the folio maps in the Mercator-Hondius atlas and the
Atlas Minor. Most of the maps were engraved by Pieter van den Keere. Cloppenburch's *Atlas* is dedicated to the States General of the United Provinces and Prince
Frederik Hendrik of Orange (1584–1647), *stadhouder* of Holland

Occurrence in atlases
353:01/02 Atlas, Evertsz. Cloppenburch, 1630/36: 19 K2r 75
353:11 Atlas, Evertsz. Cloppenburch, 1632: 19 K2r 75
353:21 Atlas, Janssonius van Waesbergen, 1673: 114 blank
353:31 Nieuwe en beknopte Uytbeeldinge en Vertooninge der gantscher Aerdbodem, Janssonius van Waesbergen, 1676: 122 blank
353:41/42 Atlas Portatif..., Du Sauzet, 1734: 195 blank

40.1   **[5112:1.1] England (Southwest) and South Wales**
CORNVBIA, | DEVONIA, SOMER- | SETVS, DORCESTRIA, |
WILTONIA, GLOCESTRIA, | MONVMETHA, GLAMORG- |
AN, CAERMARDEN, PEN- | BROK, CARDIGAN, RAD- | NOR,
BREKNOKE, HE- | REFORDIA, & WI- | GORNIA
Cornwall, Devon, Somerset, Dorcester, Wiltshire, Gloucestershire,
Monmouthshire, Glamorgan, Carmarthenshire, Pembroke, Cardi-
gan, Radnor, Breconshire, Herefordshire and Worcestershire
Per Gerardum Mercatorem.
36.5 x 46 cm.

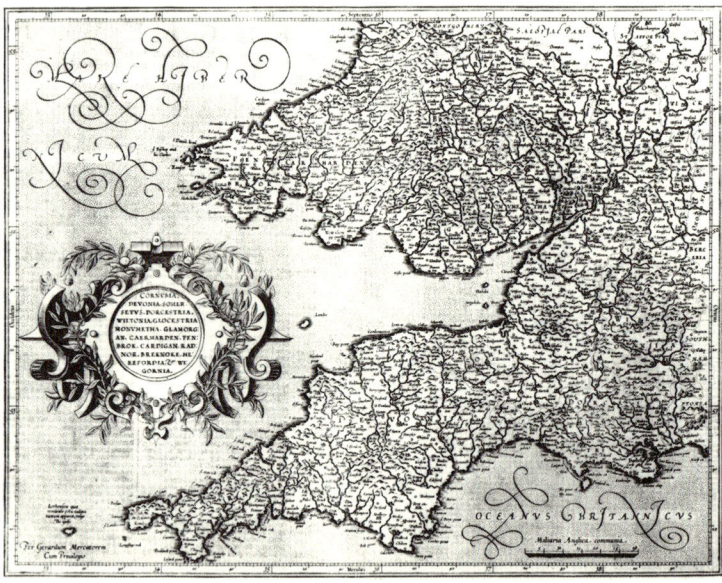

Notes   The maps for the *Atlas* of Gerard Mercator (1512-1594) – the first book
with the title atlas – were published in five parts between 1585 and 1595. The fifth
part (maps of the British Isles, Northern and Eastern Europe) was prepared for
publication by Gerard's son Rumold Mercator in 1595 and lacks a title page.

Occurrence in atlases
1:011/12 Atlas, Mercator, 1595: 20 XV
1:101 Hondius-Claesz., 1606: 21 2A 71-72
1:102 Atlas, Hondius-Claesz., 1607-08: 22 2A 69-70
1:111 Atlas, Hondius, 1609: 22 2A 69-70
1:103 Atlas, Hondius, 1611-12: 22 2B 71-72
1:104 Atlas, Hondius jr, 1613-19: 21 2D 69-70
1:112 Atlas,l Hondius jr, 1613-16: 22 2C 77-78
1:113 Atlas, Hondius jr, 1619: 22 2B 71-72
1:105 Atlas, Hondius, 1623: 21 2D 71-72
1:114 Atlas, Hondius, 1628: 22 2L 133-136

1:107 Atlas, Hondius, 1630: 22 2E 71-72
1:311 Atlas, Hondius, 1633: VI 23 2L 133-136
1:321/22 Atlas, Janssonius-Hondius, 1633: 13 N 49-52
1:331 Atlas, Janssonius-Hondius, 1634: 15 P 29-30

40.2   [5112:1.2] England (Southwest) and South Wales
CORNVBIA, DEVONIA, | SOMERSETVS, DORCESTRIA, |
WILTONIA, GLOCESTRIA, MONV- | METHA, CLAMOR-
GAN, CAERMARDE<u>N</u>, | PENBROK, CARDIGAN, RADNOR,
BRE- | KNOKE, HEREFORDIA et WIGORNIA
Cornwall, Devon, Somerset, Dorcester, Wiltshire, Gloucestershire,
Monmouthshire, Glamorgan, Carmarthenshire, Pembroke, Cardi-
gan, Radnor, Breconshire, Herefordshire and Worcestershire

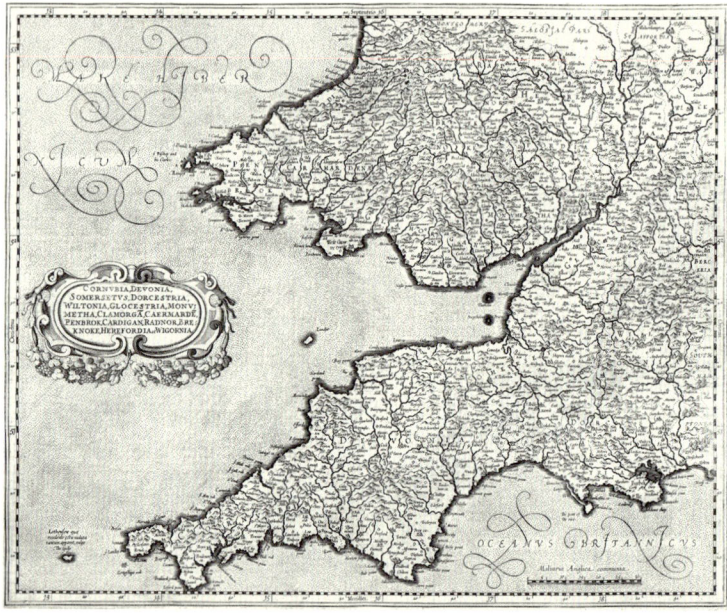

Notes   This map first appeared in the first English edition of the Mercator atlas
by Hondius and Janssonius. Mercator's plates of the maps of England have been
corrected and improved with new vignettes. The name of Mercator was effaced
on some, the name of Henricus Hondius added on others.

Occurrence in atlases
1:341 Hondius-Janssonius, 1636-41: VI 10 Y 63-64
1:401 Atlas Novus, Janssonius-Hondius, 1638: VI 23 2A
1:411/2 Nouveau Theatre du Monde, Hondius, 1639-42: VI 22 X

41   [5112:342] England (Southwest)
      Cornub. | Devonia | Somerset | etc.
      Cornwall, Devon, Somerset, etc.
      9.5 X 13.5 cm.

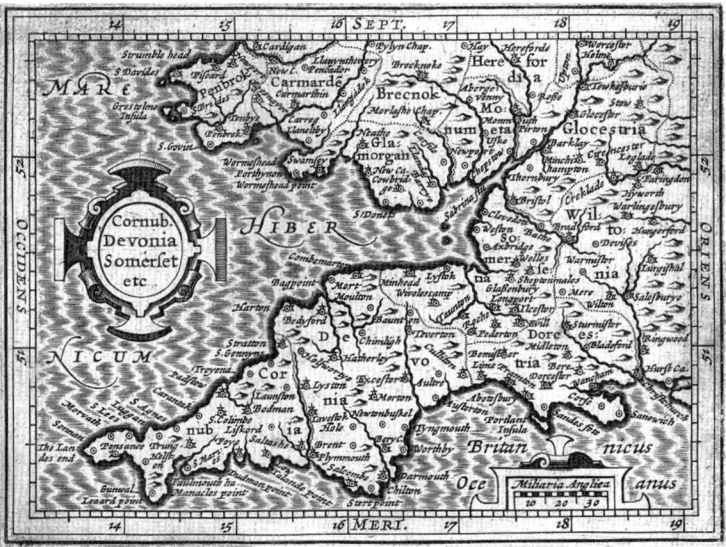

Notes   This map is one of a new series of engraved plates which were made for
the editions of Bertius's *Tabulae Geographicae Contractae*, to be published by Jodocus Hondius junior. The plates were used to illustrate some other books with
maps, such as Paullus Merula's *Cosmographia Generalis*, printed in Leiden by Isaac
Elsevier for Jodocus Hondius junior.

Occurrence in atlases

342:01 Tabulae Geographicae Contractae, Bertius, 1616/18: 30 I8v 144

342:11 La Geographie Racourcie de Pierre Bertius, Hondius jr, 1618: 30 I8v 144

342:21 Atlas Minor, J. Blaeu, 1637: 89

42   **[5112:351] England (Southwest)**
     Cornub. | Devonia, | Somerset | etc.
     Cornwall, Devon, Somerset, etc.
     13 X 18.5 cm.

Notes   The first mention of this atlas is in the *Const ende caert-register*, the 1609 map catalogue by Cornelis Claesz., as "*Atlas Minor Gerardi Mercatoris à I. Hondio [...] Illustratus in 4o. Amsterodami apud Cornelium Nicolai, 1608.*"

Occurrence in atlases

351:01 Atlas Minor, Hondius-Claesz.-Jansz., [1607]: 20 K4r
351:11 Atlas Minor, Hondius-Claesz.-Jansz., 1608 [Fr.]): 20 K4r 79
351:21 Atlas Minor, Hondius-Claesz.-Jansz., 1609: 20 M2r 91
351:02 Atlas Minor, Hondius-Claesz.-Jansz., 1610: 21 L2r 83
351:12/13 Atlas Minor, Hondius-Claesz.-Jansz., 1613/14: 20 K4r 79
351:03 Atlas Minor, Jansz., 1620-21: 21 L2r 83
351:31 Historia Mundi or Mercator's Atlas, Cotes, 1635-39: 21 K3r 101

43.1   [5112:352.1] England (Southwest)
Cornubia, Devonia, | Somersetus, Dorcestria, | Wiltonia, Glocestria, | Monumetha, Glamorgan, | Caermarden, Penbrok, | Breknoke, et Herefordia.

Cornwall, Devon, Somerset, Dorcester, Wiltshire, Gloucestershire, Monmouthshire, Glamorgan, Carmarthenshire, Pembroke, Breconshire and Herefordshire

14.5 X 20 cm.

Notes   Between 1621 and 1625 the copperplates of the *Atlas Minor* were sold to parties in England. Therefore, Johannes Janssonius, who wanted to publish a new edition of the *Atlas Minor*, had the engraver Pieter van den Keere make a new set of copperplates. The first edition of this new *Atlas Minor* was published in 1628.

Occurrence in atlases

352:01 Atlas Minor, Janssonius, 1628: 18 I4r 71
352:11 Atlas Minor, Janssonius, 1630: 18 L3 85
352:31 Atlas Minor, Janssonius, 1631: 18 K1r 73
352:02 Atlas Minor, Janssonius, 1634: 18 I4r 71
352:32/33 Atlas Minor, Janssonius, 1648-51: VI 8 D4r 31

43.2   **[5112:352.2] England (Southwest)**
**Les Comtés de | WILT, DORSET, | SOMERSET, | DEVON, | COR-
NOUAILLE | et autres.**
Wiltshire, Dorset, Somerset, Devon, Cornwall and others

Notes   This map appeared in the *Atlas soulagé de son gros & pesant fardeau*, published by Pieter van der Aa. Almost all the maps are printed from reworked plates
of Janssonius's *Atlas Minor*. The titles and scale were translated into French. Several Latin texts on the maps have been removed, as have the Latin names of the
wind directions in the borders. The cartouches have been modernized and windroses added. Other modernizations are the removal of ships and sea monsters,
and erasing names in curled letters and replacing them with Roman type letters.
Latin names of seas and countries are often translated into French.

Occurrence in atlases
352:51.2-9 Atlas soulagé..., Van der Aa, c. 1714: v4 3 blank

44   **[5112:353] England (Southwest)**
CORNVBIA | DEVONIA, SOMER- | SETVS, DORCEStIA, |
WIlTONIA, GLOCESTRA | MONVMETHA, GLAMOR- | GAN,
CAERMARDEN, PEN- | BROK, CARDIGAN, RAD- | NOR,
BREKNOKE, HE- | REFORDIA, & WI- | GORNIA
Cornwall, Devon, Somerset, Dorcester, Wiltshire, Gloucestershire,
Monmouthshire, Glamorgan, Carmarthenshire, Pembroke, Cardi-
gan, Radnor, Breconshire, Herefordshire and Worcestershire
Petrus Kærius Cælavit.
18.5 x 25.5 cm.

Notes   This map appeared in the *Atlas* of Jan Evertsz. Cloppenburch. This new
edition of Mercator's atlas was a competitive one. Its newly engraved maps were
of a size that fell in between the folio maps in the Mercator-Hondius atlas and the
Atlas Minor. Most of the maps were engraved by Pieter van den Keere. Cloppenburch's *Atlas* is dedicated to the States General of the United Provinces and Prince
Frederik Hendrik of Orange (1584–1647), *stadhouder* of Holland.

Occurrence in atlases
353:01/02 Atlas, Evertsz. Cloppenburch, 1630/36: 20 K4r 79
353:11 Atlas, Evertsz. Cloppenburch, 1632: 20 K4r 79
353:21 Atlas, Janssonius van Waesbergen, 1673: 111 blank
353:31 Nieuwe en beknopte Uytbeeldinge en Vertooninge der gantscher Aerdbodem,
Janssonius van Waesbergen, 1676: 119 blank
353:41/ 42 Atlas Portatif..., Du Sauzet, 1734: 192 blank

45.1 **[5113:1.1] England (West)**
**EBORACVM, | LINCOLNIA, DERBIA, | STAFFORDIA, NOT-
ING- | HAMIA, LECESTRIA, | RVTLANDIA, ET | NORFOLCIA**
Yorkshire, Lincolnshire, Derbyshire, Staffordshire, Nottinghamshire,
Leicestershire, Rutland and Norfolk
Per Gerardum Mercatorem.
35 x 41 cm.

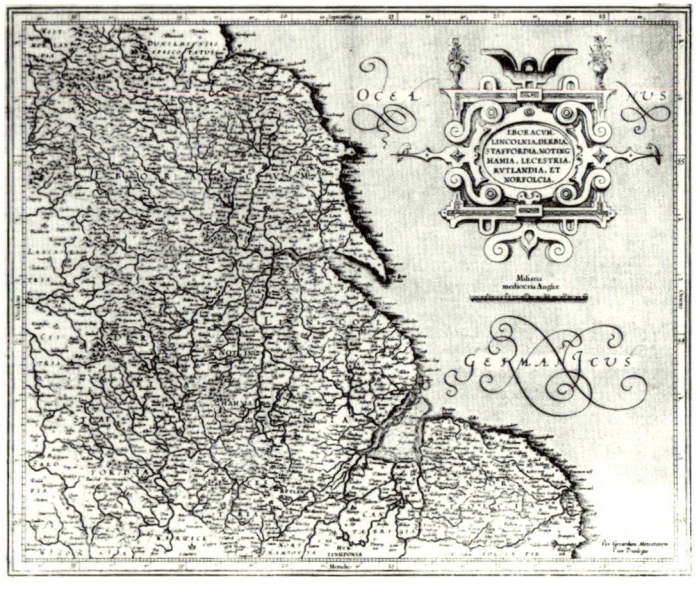

Notes This map, which was first published in Mercator's *Atlas*, 1595 edition,
has a graticule on the edges of the map.

Occurrence in atlases 1:011/12 Atlas, Mercator, 1595: 21 XVI
1:101 Hondius-Claesz., 1606: 22 2B 73-74
1:102 Atlas, Hondius-Claesz., 1607-08: 23 2B 71-72
1:111 Atlas, Hondius, 1609: 23 2B 71-72
1:103 Atlas, Hondius, 1611-12: 23 2C 73-74
1:104 Atlas, Hondius jr, 1613-19: 23 2F 73-74
1:112 Atlas, Hondius jr, 1613-16: 23 2D 79-80
1:113 Atlas, Hondius jr, 1619: 23 2C 73-74
1:105 Atlas, Hondius, 1623: 23 2F 73-
1:114 Atlas, Hondius, 1628: 23 2M 137-140
1:107 Atlas, Hondius, 1630: 24 2G 75-76
1:311 Atlas, Hondius, 1633: VI 24 2M 137-140
1:321/22 Atlas, Janssonius-Hondius, 1633: 14 O 53-56
1:331 Atlas, Janssonius-Hondius, 1634: 16 Q 31-32

45.2   [5113:1.2] England (West)
**EBORACVM, | LINCOLNIA, DERBIA, | STAFFORDIA, NOT-
ING- | HAMIA, LECESTRIA, | RVTLANDIA, ET | NORFOL-
CIA**
Yorkshire, Lincolnshire, Derbyshire, Staffordshire, Nottinghamshire,
Leicestershire, Rutland and Norfolk

Notes   This map first appeared in the first English edition of the Mercator atlas
by Hondius and Janssonius. Mercator's plates of the maps of England have been
corrected and improved with new vignettes. The name of Mercator was effaced
on some, the name of Henricus Hondius added on others.

Occurrence in atlases
1:341 Hondius-Janssonius, 1636-41: VI 11 Y 65-66
1:401 Atlas Novus, Janssonius-Hondius, 1638: VI 22 Z
1:411/2 Nouveau Theatre du Monde, Hondius, 1639-42: VI 23 Y

46   [5113:342] England (Northeast)
       Eboracum Lin- | colnia Derbia | Staffordia etc.
       Yorkshire, Lincolnshire, Derbyshire, Staffordshire, etc.
       9.5 X 13.5 cm.

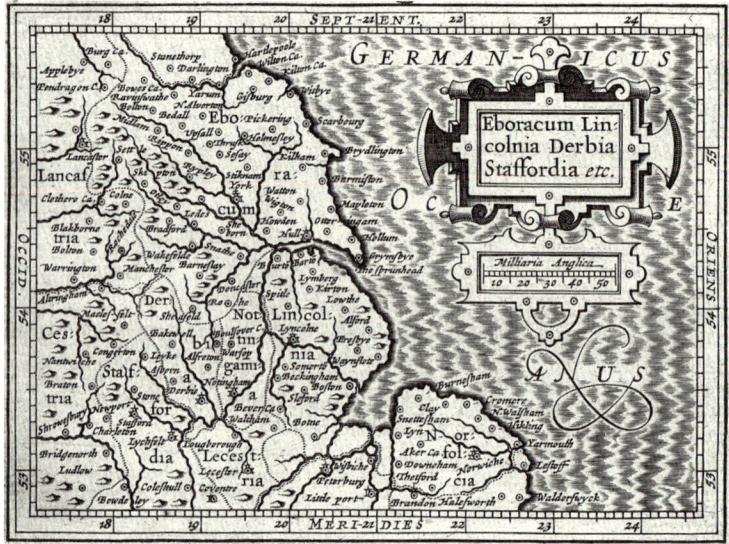

Notes This map is one of a new engraved series of plates which were made for the editions of Bertius's *Tabulae Geographicae Contractae*, to be published by Jodocus Hondius junior. The plates were used to illustrate some other books with maps, such as Paullus Merula's *Cosmographia Generalis*, printed in Leiden by Isaac Elsevier for Jodocus Hondius junior.

Occurrence in atlases

342:01 Tabulae Geographicae Contractae, Bertius, 1616/18: 31 Kiv 146
342:11 La Geographie Racourcie de Pierre Bertius, Hondius jr, 1618: 31 Kiv 146
342:21 Atlas Minor, J. Blaeu, 1637: 90

47   [5113:351] England (Northeast)
EBORACUM | Lincolnia Der | bia, Stafford, | etc.
Yorkshire, Lincolnshire, Derbyshire, Staffordshire, etc.
13 X 17 cm.

Notes   In 1607, a year after publishing Mercator's atlas in folio, Hondius published it in a reduced edition, the *Atlas Minor*. In so doing, he followed a tradi-
tion that had begun in Antwerp in 1577 with the *Epitome*, a reduced version of
Ortelius's *Theatrum Orbis Terrarum*.

Occurrence in atlases
351:01 Atlas Minor, Hondius-Claesz.-Jansz., [1607]: 21 K2r
351:11 Atlas Minor, Hondius-Claesz.-Jansz., 1608 [Fr.]): 21 L2r 83
351:21 Atlas Minor, Hondius-Claesz.-Jansz., 1609: 21 M4r 95
351:02 Atlas Minor, Hondius-Claesz.-Jansz., 1610: 22 L4r 87
351:12/13 Atlas Minor, Hondius-Claesz.-Jansz., 1613/14: 21 L2r 83
351:03 Atlas Minor, Jansz., 1620-21: 22 L4r 87
351:31 Historia Mundi or Mercator's Atlas, Cotes, 1635-39: 22 K6r 107

48.1   [5113:352.1] **England (Northeast)**
Eboracum, | Lincolnia, Derbia, | Staffordia, Notin- | ghamia, Leices-
tria, | Rutlandia, et | Norfolcia.
Yorkshire, Lincolnshire, Derbyshire, Staffordshire, Nottinghamshire,
Leicestershire, Rutland and Norfolk
14.5 X 20 cm.

Notes   Between 1621 and 1625 the copperplates of the *Atlas Minor* were sold to
parties in England. Therefore, Johannes Janssonius, who wanted to publish a new
edition of the *Atlas Minor*, had the engraver Pieter van den Keere make a new set
of copperplates. The first edition of this new *Atlas Minor* was published in 1628.

Occurrence in atlases
352:01 Atlas Minor, Janssonius, 1628: 19 K2r 75
352:11 Atlas Minor, Janssonius, 1630: 19 M2 91
352:31 Atlas Minor, Janssonius, 1631: 19 K3r 77
352:02 Atlas Minor, Janssonius, 1634: 19 K2r 75
352:32/33 Atlas Minor, Janssonius, 1648-51: VI 11 F2r 43

48.2   [5113:352.2] England (Northeast)
Les Comtés de | LEICESTER, | RUTLAND, LINCOLN, | NOT-
TINGHAM, | DARBY, STAFFORD | et autres.
Leicestershire, Rutland, Lincolnshire, Nottinghamshire, Derbyshire,
Staffordshire and others

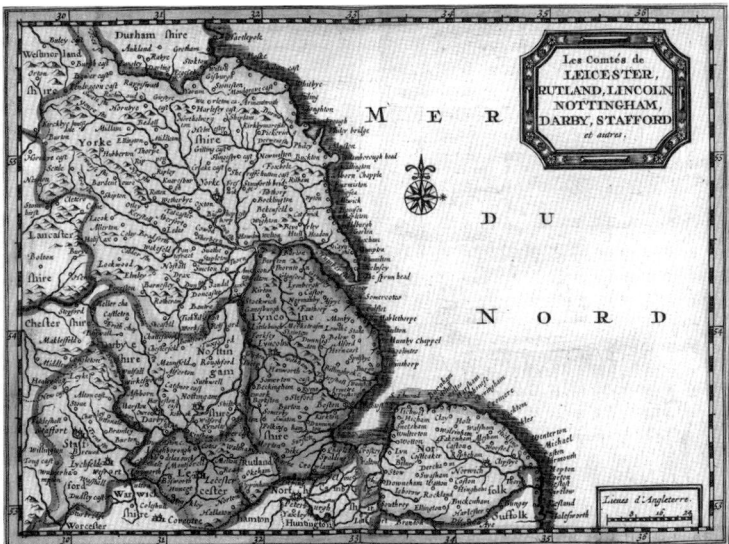

Notes   This map appeared in the *Atlas soulagé de son gros & pesant fardeau*, published by Pieter van der Aa. Almost all the maps are printed from reworked plates
of Janssonius's *Atlas Minor*. The titles and scale were translated into French. Several Latin texts on the maps have been removed, as have the Latin names of the
wind directions in the borders. The cartouches have been modernized and windroses added. Other modernizations are the removal of ships and sea monsters,
and erasing names in curled letters and replacing them with Roman type letters.
Latin names of seas and countries are often translated into French.

Occurrence in atlases

352:51.2-9 Atlas soulagé…, Van der Aa, c. 1714: v4 8 blank

49 [5113:353] England (Northeast)
EBORACUM, LINCO- | LNIA, DERBIA, STAF- | FORDIA, NO-
TINGHA- | MIA, LECESTRIA, | RUTLANDIA, ET | NORFOL-
CIA
Yorkshire, Lincolnshire, Derbyshire, Staffordshire, Nottinghamshire,
Leicestershire, Rutland and Norfolk
Petrus Kærius Cælavit.
18.5 X 25.5 cm.

Notes This map appeared in the *Atlas* of Jan Evertsz. Cloppenburch. This new
edition of Mercator's atlas was a competitive one. Its newly engraved maps were
of a size that fell in between the folio maps in the Mercator-Hondius atlas and the
Atlas Minor. Most of the maps were engraved by Pieter van den Keere. Cloppenburch's *Atlas* is dedicated to the States General of the United Provinces and Prince
Frederik Hendrik of Orange (1584–1647), *stadhouder* of Holland.

Occurrence in atlases
353:01/02 Atlas, Evertsz. Cloppenburch, 1630/36: 21 L2r 83
353:11 Atlas, Evertsz. Cloppenburch, 1632: 21 L2r 83
353:21 Atlas, Janssonius van Waesbergen, 1673: 112 blank
353:31 Nieuwe en beknopte Uytbeeldinge en Vertooninge der gantscher Aerdbodem, Janssonius van Waesbergen, 1676: 120 blank
353:41/42 Atlas Portatif..., Du Sauzet, 1734: 194 blank

50.1   [5114:1.1] England (Southeast)
Warwicum, | Northhamtonia, | Huntingdonia, Can- | tabrigia, Suf-
folcia, Ox- | onium, Buckinghamia, | Bedfordia, Hartfordia, | Essexia,
Berceria, Midd- | elsexia, Southhamtonia | Surria, Cantium & |
Southsexia
Warwickshire, Northamptonshire, Huntingdonshire, Cambridgeshire, Suffolk, Oxfordshire, Buckinghamshire, Bedfordshire, Hertfordshire, Essex, Berkshire, Middlesex, Southamton, Surrey, Kent and
Sussex
37 X 46 cm.

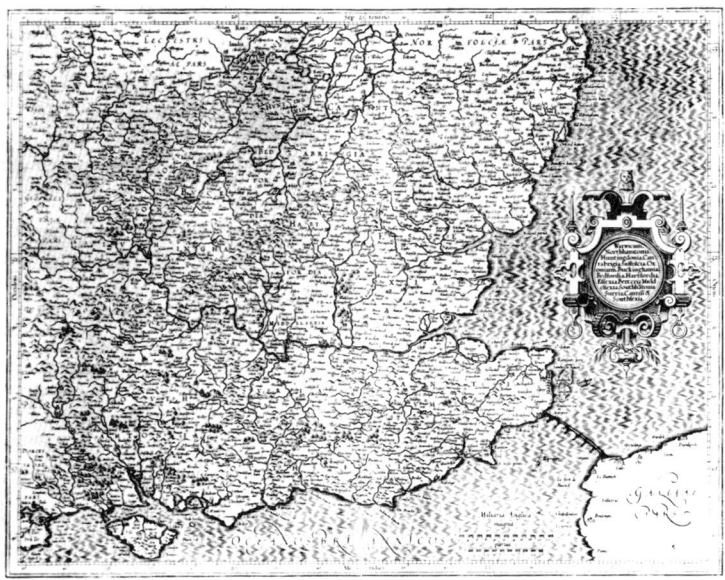

Notes   This map was first published in the 1595 edition of Mercator's *Atlas*,
which was published by his heirs, after Mercator's death in 1594. The map appears
in atlases until 1634. NB The Channel Bridge is a manuscript addition to the illustrated copy!

Occurrence in atlases
1:011/12 Atlas, Mercator, 1595: 22 XVII
1:101 Hondius-Claesz., 1606: 23 2C 75-67 MP
1:102 Atlas, Hondius-Claesz., 1607-08: 24 2C 73-74
1:111 Atlas, Hondius, 1609: 24 2C 73-74
1:103 Atlas, Hondius, 1611-12: 24 2D 75-76
1:104 Atlas, Hondius jr, 1613-19: 24 2G 75-76
1:112 Atlas,l Hondius jr, 1613-16: 24 2E 81-82
1:113 Atlas, Hondius jr, 1619: 24 2D 75-76
1:105 Atlas, Hondius, 1623: 24 2D 75-76 MP 73 as 37
1:114 Atlas, Hondius, 1628: 24 2N 141-144

1:107 Atlas, Hondius, 1630: 25 2H 77-78
1:311 Atlas, Hondius, 1633: VI 26 2N 141-144
1:321/22 Atlas, Janssonius-Hondius, 1633: 15 P 57-60
1:331 Atlas, Janssonius-Hondius, 1634: 17 R 33-34

50.2 [5114:1.2] England (Southeast)
Warwicum | Northamtonia | Huntingdonia Can | tabrigia Suffolcia
Ox | onium Buckinghamia | Bedfordia Hardfordia | Essexia Berceria
Mid | delsexia Southantonia | Surria Cantium et | Southsexia
Warwickshire, Northamptonshire, Huntingdonshire, Cambridgeshire, Suffolk, Oxfordshire, Buckinghamshire, Bedfordshire, Hertfordshire, Essex, Berkshire, Middlesex, Southamton, Surrey, Kent
and Sussex
Sumptibus Henrici Hondy

Notes This map first appeared in the first English edition of the Mercator atlas
by Hondius and Janssonius. Mercator's plates of the maps of England have been
corrected and improved with new vignettes. The name of Mercator was effaced
on some, the name of Henricus Hondius added on others.

Occurrence in atlases
1:341 Hondius-Janssonius, 1636-41: VI 13 2A 85-86
1:401 Atlas Novus, Janssonius-Hondius, 1638: VI 24 2B
1:411/2 Nouveau Theatre du Monde, Hondius, 1639-42: VI 24 Z

51   [5114:342] **England (Southeast)**
Warwicum | Northampton | Hunting. etc.
Warwickshire, Northamptonshire, Huntingdonshire, etc.
9.5 x 13.5 cm.

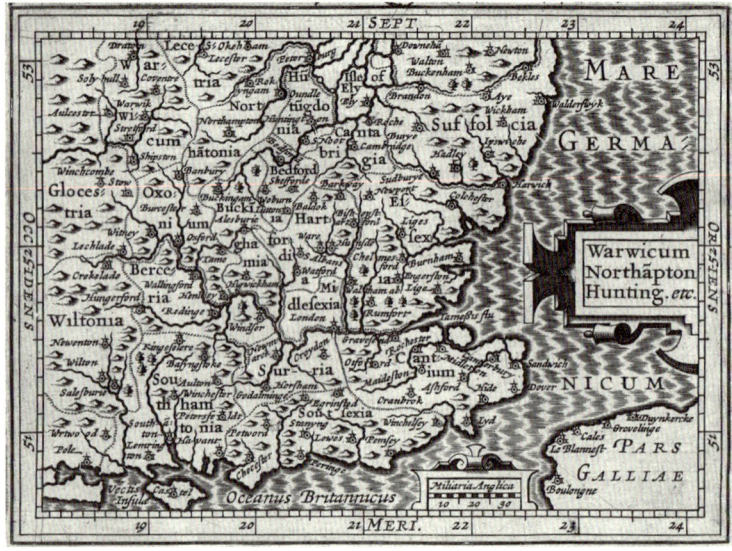

Notes   This map is one of a new engraved series of plates, which were made for the editions of Bertius's Tabulae Geographicae Contractae, to be published by Jodocus Hondius Jr. The plates were used to illustrate some other books with maps, such as Paullus Merula's Cosmographia Generalis, printed in Leiden by Isaac Elsevier for Jodocus Hondius Jr.

Occurrence in atlases

342:01 Tabulae Geographicae Contractae, Bertius, 1616/18: 32 K2v 148

342:11 La Geographie Racourcie de Pierre Bertius, Hondius jr, 1618: 32 K2v 148

342:21 Atlas Minor, J. Blaeu, 1637: 91

52 **[5114:351] England (Southeast)**
War- | wicum No | rthampton, | Huntingdon | Cantabr. | etc.
Warwickshire, Northamptonshire, Huntingdonshire, Cambridgeshire, etc.
14 X 18 cm.

Notes The first appearence in an atlas of this map, is in the *Atlas Minor* published by Hondius, Cornelis Claesz. and Jan Jansz. The first mention of this atlas
is in the *Const ende caert-register*, the 1609 map catalogue by Cornelis Claesz.,
"*Atlas Minor Gerardi Mercatoris à I. Hondio [...] Illustratus in 4o. Amsterodami
apud Cornelium Nicolai, 1608*."

Occurrence in atlases
351:01 Atlas Minor, Hondius-Claesz.-Jansz., [1607]: 22 K4r
351:11 Atlas Minor, Hondius-Claesz.-Jansz., 1608 [Fr.]): 22 L4r 87
351:21 Atlas Minor, Hondius-Claesz.-Jansz., 1609: 22 N2r 99
351:02 Atlas Minor, Hondius-Claesz.-Jansz., 1610: 23 M2r 91
351:12/13 Atlas Minor, Hondius-Claesz.-Jansz., 1613/14: 22 L4r 87
351:03 Atlas Minor, Jansz., 1620-21: 23 M2r 91
351:31 Historia Mundi or Mercator's Atlas, Cotes, 1635-39: 23 L2r 111

53.1 [5114:352.1] England (Southeast)
Warwicum North- | hamtonia, Huntingdonia, | Cantabrigia, Suf-
folcia, | Oxonium, Buckinghamia, | Bedfordia, Hartfordia, Eßexia,
| Berceria, Middelsexia, Southham- | tonia, Surria, Cantium, et
Southsexia.
Warwickshire, Northamptonshire, Huntingdonshire, Cambridgeshire, Suffolk, Oxfordshire, Buckinghamshire, Bedfordshire, Hertfordshire, Essex, Berkshire, Middlesex, Southamton, Surrey, Kent
and Sussex
15 x 20 cm.

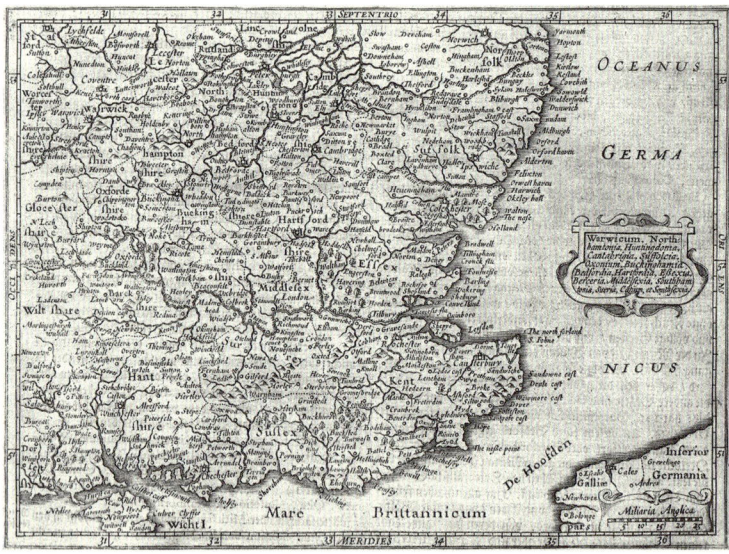

Notes Between 1621 and 1625 the copperplates of the *Atlas Minor* were sold to
parties in England. Therefore, Johannes Janssonius, who wanted to publish a new
edition of the *Atlas Minor*, had the engraver Pieter van den Keere make a new set
of copperplates. The first edition of this new *Atlas Minor* was published in 1628.

Occurrence in atlases
352:01 Atlas Minor, Janssonius, 1628: 20 K4r 79
352:11 Atlas Minor, Janssonius, 1630: 20 M4 95
352:31 Atlas Minor, Janssonius, 1631: 20 L1r 81
352:02 Atlas Minor, Janssonius, 1634: 20 K4r 79
352:32/33 Atlas Minor, Janssonius, 1648-51: vi 14 G4r 55

53.2   [5114:352.2] England (Southeast)
Les Comtés & Provinces de | KENT, MIDDLESEX, | ESSEX, SUS-
SEX, SURREY, | SOUTHAMPTON, BARCK, | CAMBRIDGE,
SUFFOLK, | BUCKINGHAM, HARFORD, | BEDFORD,
HUNTINGTON | NORTHAMPTON, OXFORD, | WARWICK
et autres.
Kent, Middlesex, Essex, Sussex, Surrey, Hampshire, Berkshire,
Cambridgeshire, Suffolk, Buckinghamshire, Hartford, Bedfordshire,
Huntingdonshire, Northamptonshire, Oxfordshire, Warwickshire
and others

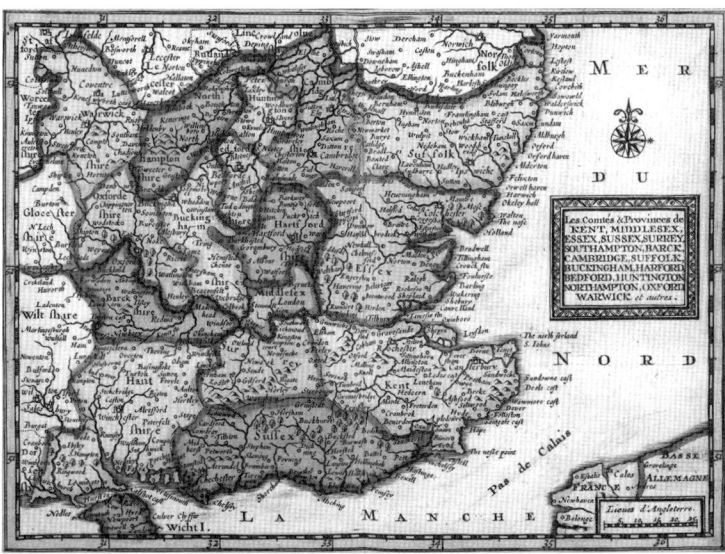

Notes   This map appeared in the *Atlas soulagé de son gros & pesant fardeau*, published by Pieter van der Aa. Almost all the maps are printed from reworked plates
of Janssonius's *Atlas Minor*. The titles and scale were translated into French. Several Latin texts on the maps have been removed, as have the Latin names of the
wind directions in the borders. The cartouches have been modernized and windroses added. Other modernizations are the removal of ships and sea monsters,
and erasing names in curled letters and replacing them with Roman type letters.
Latin names of seas and countries are often translated into French.

Occurrence in atlases
352:51.2-9 Atlas soulagé..., Van der Aa, c. 1714: v4 5 blank

54 [5114:353] England (Southeast)
Warwicum | Northhamtonia | HVNTINGDONIA CA- | NTABRI-
GIA, SVFFOL- | CIA, OXONIVM, BVCK- | INGHAMIA,
BEDFORdia | Hartfordia Essexia | BERCERI MIDELSE- | XIA,
SOVTHHAMTONIA | Surria, Cantium | Southsexia.
Warwickshire, Northamptonshire, Huntingdonshire, Cambridgeshire, Suffolk, Oxfordshire, Buckinghamshire, Bedfordshire, Hertfordshire, Essex, Berkshire, Middlesex, Southamton, Surrey, Kent
and Sussex
19 X 26 cm.

Notes This map appeared in the *Atlas* of Jan Evertsz. Cloppenburch. This new
edition of Mercator's atlas was a competitive one. Its newly engraved maps were
of a size that fell in between the folio maps in the Mercator-Hondius atlas and the
Atlas Minor. Most of the maps were engraved by Pieter van den Keere. Cloppenburch's *Atlas* is dedicated to the States General of the United Provinces and Prince
Frederik Hendrik of Orange (1584–1647), *stadhouder* of Holland.

Occurrence in atlases
353:01/02 Atlas, Evertsz. Cloppenburch, 1630/36: 22 L4r 87
353:11 Atlas, Evertsz. Cloppenburch, 1632: 22 L4r 87
353:21 Atlas, Janssonius van Waesbergen, 1673: 113 blank
353:31 Nieuwe en beknopte Uytbeeldinge en Vertooninge der gantscher Aerdbodem, Janssonius van Waesbergen, 1676: 121 blank
353:41/42 Atlas Portatif..., Du Sauzet, 1734: 193 blank

55 [5120:341(Wright)] Thames River
Tamesis. Britanniæ | nobilißimum flumen Lon- | dinum regiam
urbom | præterlabens
The Thames. The most noble river of Britain flowing past the royal
town of London.
B.W. | cælator.
8.5 x 12 cm.

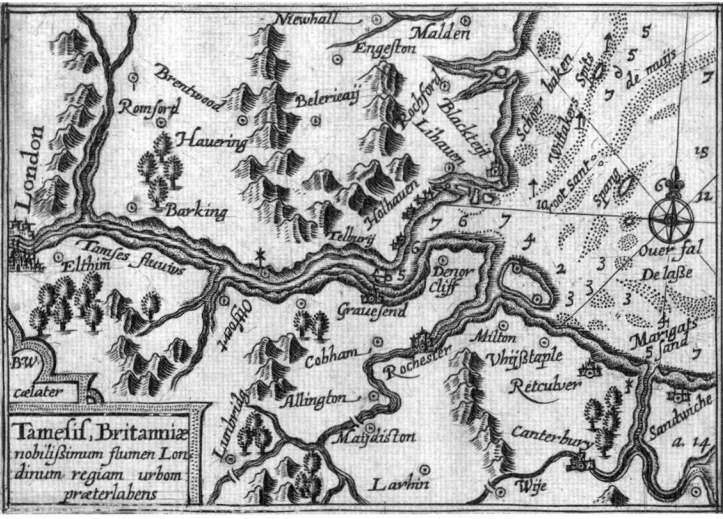

Notes   The River Thames is the second longest river in the United Kingdom and
the longest river entirely in England, rising at Thames Head in Gloucestershire,
and flowing into the North Sea at the Thames Estuary. It has a special significance
in flowing through London, the capital of the United Kingdom, although London
only includes a short part of its course. The river is tidal in London with a rise and
fall of 7 metres (23 ft) and becomes non-tidal at Teddington Lock. The catchment
area covers a large part of South Eastern and Western England and the river is fed
by over 20 tributaries. The river contains over 80 islands, and having both seawater
and freshwater stretches supports a variety of wildlife.

Occurrence in atlases
341:54 Tabulae Geographicae Contractae, C.J. Visscher, 1649: 13 a.14

56.1   [5200:1.1] Kent
PROVINCIÆ | CANTII | Vulgo | KENDT | Nova Descriptio
New map of the county Cantium, in popular speech Kent
38 x 50 cm.

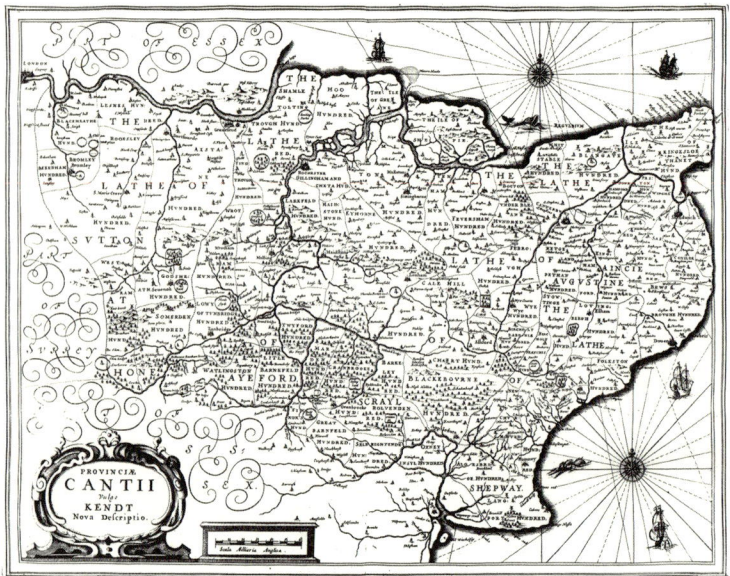

Notes   Because of its abundance of orchards and hop gardens, Kent is widely
known as "The Garden of England".

Occurrence in atlases
1:432 Des Nieuwen Atlantis Aenhang, Janssonius, 1644: 11 l
1:434/36 Nieuwen Atlas... Het Vierde deel, Janssonius, 1647-49/1658: v4 4 2H

56.2   [5200:1.2] Kent
CANTIVM | Vernacule | KENT
In the vernacular Kent
Amstelodami | Apud Ioannem Ianßonium

Notes   Kent, originally Cantia, is a county in southeast England, and is one of the home counties. The "Home counties" refers to the counties that border or surround London, England but not including the United Kingdom's capital city itself.

Occurrence in atlases
1:403/05 Atlas Novus, Janssonius, 1647/1657-62: v4 5 Y 77-78
1:414/15 Le Nouvel Atlas… Tome Quatrieme, Janssonius, 1646-49: v4 5 2C 87-88
1:425 Novus Atlas, Janssonius, 1647-49: v4 5 2F 105-106
1:434/36 Nieuwen Atlas… Het Vierde deel, Janssonius, 1647-49/1658: v4 4 2H
1:407 Atlas Contractus, Janssonius, 1666: v1 76
1:408 Atlas, Janssonius, after c. 1680: v3 4

57   [5200:2] Kent
CANTIVM | Vernacule | KENT
In the vernacular Kent
38 x 53 cm.

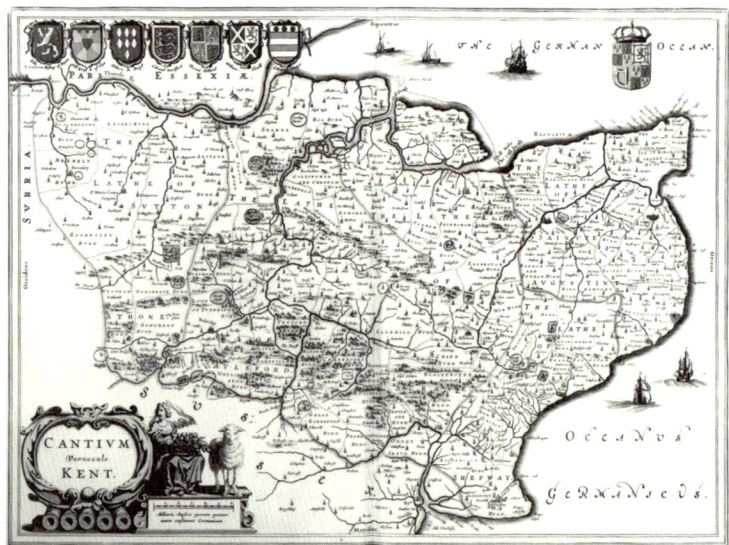

Notes   The coats of arms of the dukes of Kent and the royal family are placed in the top corners. The map has been copied from Speed's *Theatre*, edition after 1623, and was specially made for the atlas of England, which Joan Blaeu in 1645 joined as a fourth part to his *Atlas novus*.

Occurrence in atlases

2:301 Theatrum Orbis Terrarum sive Atlas Novus Pars Quarta, J. Blaeu, 1646: 14 3G 181-182

2:302-3 Theatrum Orbis Terrarum sive Atlas Novus Pars Quarta, J. Blaeu, 1646-48: 14 3B 153-154

2:311 Le Theatre du Monde ou Nouvel Atlas, Quatriesme Partie, J. Blaeu: 14 3A 157-158

2:312 Cinquème Volume de la Geographie Blaviane, J. Blaeu, 1663-67: 14 2V 131-132

2:321 Toonneel des Aerdycks oft Nieuwe Atlas... Vierde deel, J. Blaeu, 1648: 14 3F 169-170

2:322 Toonneel des Aerdycks oft Nieuwe Atlas... Vierde deel, J. Blaeu, 1648: 14 3X 143-144

2:331 Novus Atlas and Atlas Major (Vierter Teil), J. Blaeu, 1645-48: 14 3G 177-178

Nuevo Atlas del Reyno de Inglaterra, J. Blaeu, 1645/48: 14 3F 165-166

References   Van der Krogt 2002 18:23.

58   [5200:373] Kent, Sussex, Surrey, and Middlesex
      Cantii, South | sexiæ, Surriæ, et | Middlesexiæ co<u>m</u>.
      Kent, Sussex, Surrey and Middlesex
      8.5 x 12 cm.

Notes   This map is from a collection of 44 maps of the British Isles engraved by
Pieter van den Keere. The maps have a comparable size of those of the *Tabularum
Geographicarum*, published by Pieter Bertius, for which Van den Keere engraved
many maps. Although the maps of Van den Keere form one collection, no title-
page is known.

Occurrence in atlases
373:01 Atlas of the British Isles, Van den Keere, c. 1605: 9
373:02 Britannia, Camden, 1617: 8 N2v 196

References   Skelton 1970, 4.

59 [5210:1] Sussex
SVTHSEXIA, | Vernacule | SUSSEX
In the vernacular Sussex
Amstelodami | Apud Ioannem Ianßonium
38 x 52 cm.

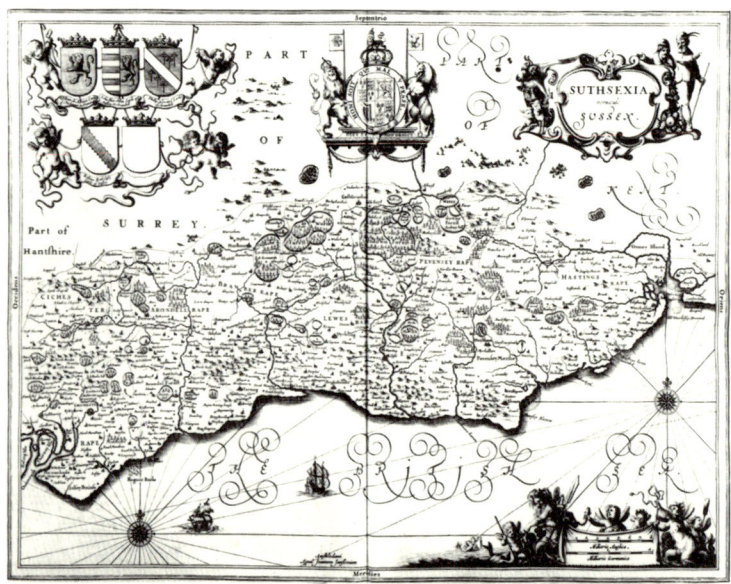

Notes   Above left are some coats of arms, one of which is empty. In the middle is the royal coat of arms. The motto is 'Honi soit qui mal y pense' (Shame be to him who thinks evil of it), the motto of the Order of the Garter. Beneath the coat of arms the motto of the royal family: 'Dieu et mon droit' (God and my right).

Occurrence in atlases

1:403/05 Atlas Novus, Janssonius, 1647/1657-62: v4 6 2C 89-90

1:414/15 Le Nouvel Atlas... Tome Quatrieme, Janssonius, 1646-49: v4 6 2G 101-102

1:425 Novus Atlas, Janssonius, 1647-49: v4 6 2K 119-120

1:434/36 Nieuwen Atlas... Het Vierde deel, Janssonius, 1647-49/1658: v4 6 2I 101-102

1:408 Atlas, Janssonius, after c. 1680: v3 5

60   [5210:2] Sussex
SVTHSEXIA, | Vernacule SUSSEX
In the vernacular Sussex
38 x 52 cm.

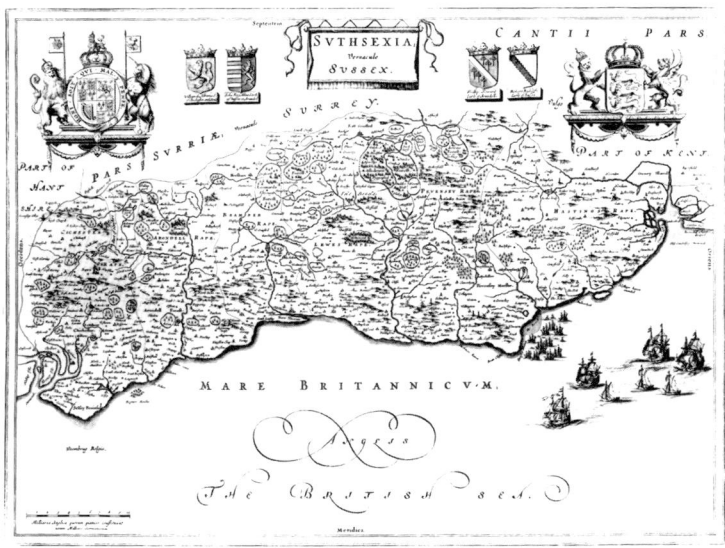

Notes   At the centre of the map, the coats of arms of the earls of Arundel and
Sussex are drawn. The map has been copied from Speeds *Theatre*, edition after
1623, and is specially made for the atlas of England, which Joan Blaeu in 1645 as a
fourth part joined to his *Atlas Novus*.

Occurrence in atlases

2:301 Theatrum Orbis Terrarum sive Atlas Novus Pars Quarta, J. Blaeu, 1646: 13
3D 173-174
2:302-3 Theatrum Orbis Terrarum sive Atlas Novus Pars Quarta, J. Blaeu, 1646-
48: 13 2Y 145-146
2:311 Le Theatre du Monde ou Nouvel Atlas, Quatriesme Partie, J. Blaeu: 13 2Y
151-152
2:312 Cinquème Volume de la Geographie Blaviane, J. Blaeu, 1663-67: 13 2S 125-126
2:321 Toonneel des Aerdycks oft Nieuwe Atlas... Vierde deel, J. Blaeu, 1648: 13
3C 161-162
2:322 Toonneel des Aerdycks oft Nieuwe Atlas... Vierde deel, J. Blaeu, 1648: 13
2T 137-138
2:331 Novus Atlas and Atlas Major (Vierter Teil), J. Blaeu, 1645-48: 13 3D 169-170
Nuevo Atlas del Reyno de Inglaterra, J. Blaeu, 1645/48: 13 3C 157-158

References   Van der Krogt 2002 18:22.

61   **[5215:1] Surrey**
SURRIA. | vernacule | SURREY
In the vernacular Surrey
38.5 x 50 cm.

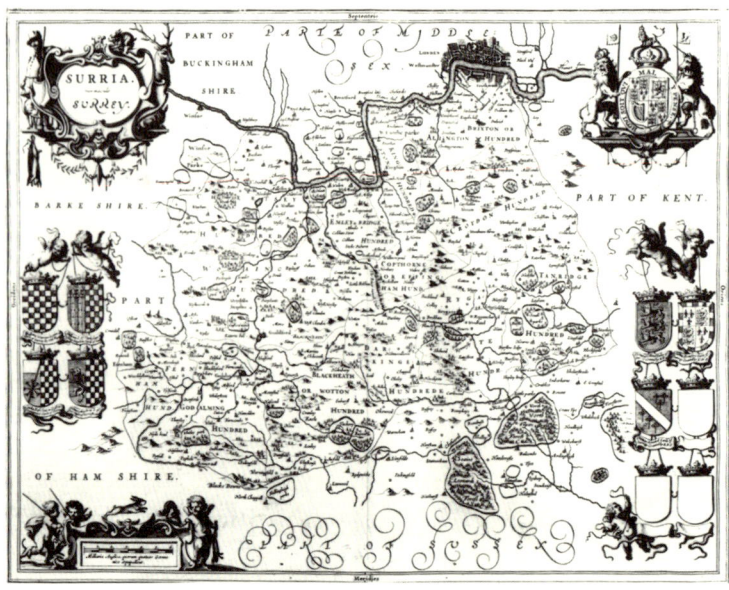

Notes   The map contains several coats of arms, three of which are empty. The coat of arms above right is the royal coat of arms with the motto' Honi soit qui mal y pense', which means 'Shame be to him who thinks evil of it' and is the motto of the Order of the Garter.

Occurrence in atlases
1:403/05 Atlas Novus, Janssonius, 1647/1657-62: v4 7 2E 95-96
1:414/15 Le Nouvel Atlas... Tome Quatrieme, Janssonius, 1646-49: v4 7 2I 107-108
1:425 Novus Atlas, Janssonius, 1647-49: v4 7 2N 129-130
1:434/36 Nieuwen Atlas... Het Vierde deel, Janssonius, 1647-49/1658: v4 7 2K 103-104
1:408 Atlas, Janssonius, after c. 1680: v3 6

62   [5215:2] Surrey
SVRRIA | Vernacule | SVRREY
In the vernacular Surrey
38 x 50 cm.

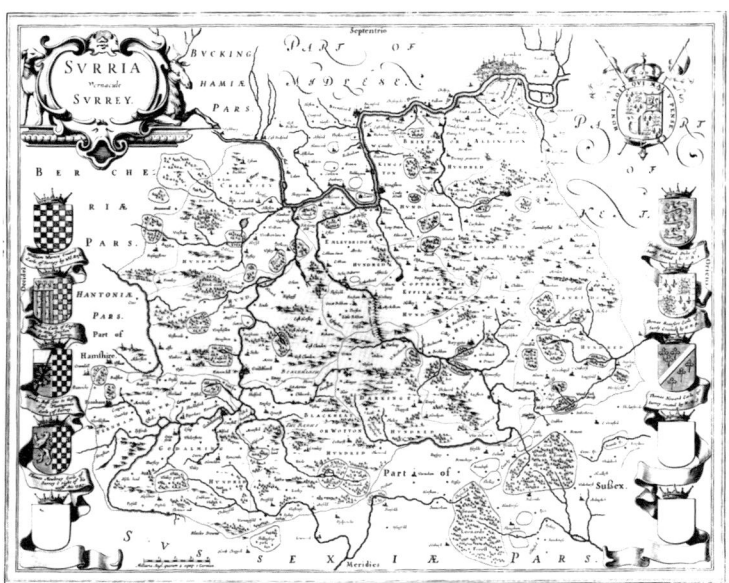

Notes   On the left and right sides are the coats of arms of the earls of Surrey.
The map has been copied from Speed's *Theatre*, edition after 1623, and is specially
made for the atlas of England, which Joan Blaeu in 1645 joined as a fourth part
to his *Atlas novus*.

Occurrence in atlases

2:301 Theatrum Orbis Terrarum sive Atlas Novus Pars Quarta, J. Blaeu, 1646: 12
3B 167-168

2:302-3 Theatrum Orbis Terrarum sive Atlas Novus Pars Quarta, J. Blaeu, 1646-
48: 12 2V 141-142

2:311 Le Theatre du Monde ou Nouvel Atlas, Quatriesme Partie, J. Blaeu: 12 2V
145-146

2:312 Cinquème Volume de la Geographie Blaviane, J. Blaeu, 1663-67: 12 2Q 121-
122

2:321 Toonneel des Aerdycks oft Nieuwe Atlas... Vierde deel, J. Blaeu, 1648: 12
3A 155-156

2:322 Toonneel des Aerdycks oft Nieuwe Atlas... Vierde deel, J. Blaeu, 1648: 12
blank

2:331 Novus Atlas and Atlas Major (Vierter Teil), J. Blaeu, 1645-48: 12 3B 163-164
Nuevo Atlas del Reyno de Inglaterra, J. Blaeu, 1645/48: 12 3A 153-154

References   Van der Krogt 2002 18:21.

63   [5220:1] Hampshire
HANTONIÆ | COMITATUS | Cum BERCHERIA
Hampshire with Berkshire
Amstelodami | Apud Ioannem Ianßonium
44 X 55 cm.

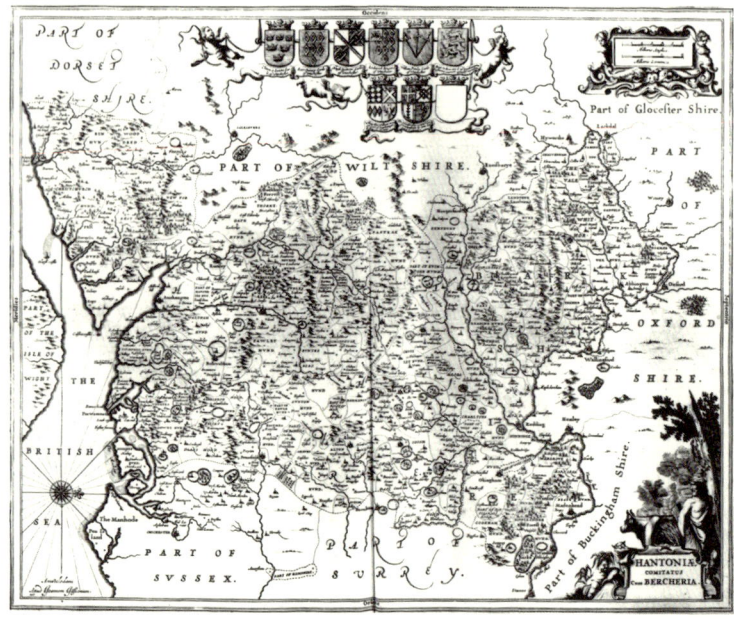

Notes   The map first appeared in Janssonius' *Atlas Novus* from 1647. The unusual western orientation of this map is remarkable.

Occurrence in atlases

1:403/05 Atlas Novus, Janssonius, 1647/1657-62: v4 8 2G 99-100

1:414/15 Le Nouvel Atlas... Tome Quatrieme, Janssonius, 1646-49: v4 8 2L 111-112

1:425 Novus Atlas, Janssonius, 1647-49: v4 8 2P 133-134

1:434/36 Nieuwen Atlas... Het Vierde deel, Janssonius, 1647-49/1658: v4 8 2L 105-106

1:408 Atlas, Janssonius, after c. 1680: v3 7

64   [5220:2] Hampshire
HANTONIA | SIVE | SOVTHANTONENSIS | COMITATVS |
Vulgo | HANT-SHIRE
Hantonia, or the county of Southampton, in the vulgar tongue
Hampshire
41.5 X 50 cm.

Notes   On the left are the coats of arms of the earls of Winchester, on the right
those some earls of Southampton. The map has been copied from Speed's *Theatre*,
edition after 1623, and was specially made for the atlas of England, which Joan
Blaeu in 1645 joined as a fourth part to his *Atlas novus*.

Occurrence in atlases   2:301 Theatrum Orbis Terrarum sive Atlas Novus Pars
   Quarta, J. Blaeu, 1646: 9 2S 149-150
2:302-3 Theatrum Orbis Terrarum sive Atlas Novus Pars Quarta, J. Blaeu, 1646-
48: 9 2N 123-124
2:311 Le Theatre du Monde ou Nouvel Atlas, Quatriesme Partie, J. Blaeu: 9 2O 129-130
2:312 Cinquème Volume de la Geographie Blaviane, J. Blaeu, 1663-67: 9 2K 107-108
2:321 Toonneel des Aerdycks oft Nieuwe Atlas... Vierde deel, J. Blaeu, 1648: 9 2S
139-140
2:322 Toonneel des Aerdycks oft Nieuwe Atlas... Vierde deel, J. Blaeu, 1648: 9
2M 117-118
2:331 Novus Atlas and Atlas Major (Vierter Teil), J. Blaeu, 1645-48: 9 2Q 145
Nuevo Atlas del Reyno de Inglaterra, J. Blaeu, 1645/48: 9 2R 135-136

References   Van der Krogt 2002 18:18.

65 [5220:373] Hampshire
SOUT | HAMTONIÆ.
Hampshire
8.5 X 12 cm.

Notes This map is from a collection of 44 maps of the British Isles, engraved by
Pieter van den Keere. The maps are comparable in size to those of the *Tabularum
Geographicarum*, published by Pieter Bertius, for which Van den Keere engraved
many maps. Although the maps of Van den Keere form one collection, no title-
page is known.

Occurrence in atlases
373:01 Atlas of the British Isles, Van den Keere, c. 1605: 6
373:02 Britannia, Camden, 1617: 7 K7r 157

References Skelton 1970, 4.

66   [5225:2] Berkshire
BERCHERIA | Vernacule | BARKSHIRE
In the vernacular Berkshire
38 x 50 cm.

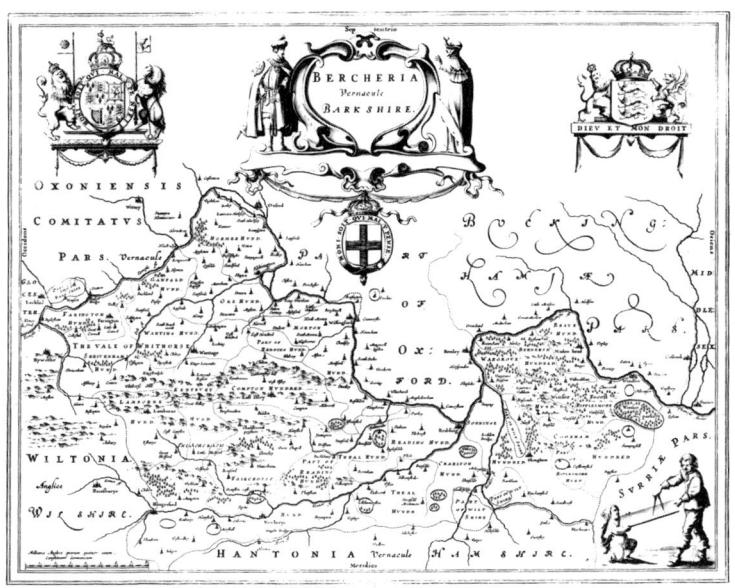

Notes   The coat of arms under the cartouche is the old coat of arms of England. This coat of arms is surrounded, like that of the king, by a garter with the motto 'Honi soit qui mal y pense' (Shame be to him who thinks evil of it). This is the symbol of Order of the Garter, which was founded in 1348 by Edward III in Windsor (right on the map). The map has been copied from Speed's *Theatre*, edition after 1623, and was specially made for the atlas of England, which Joan Blaeu in 1645 joined as a fourth part to his *Atlas novus*.

Occurrence in atlases   2:301 Theatrum Orbis Terrarum sive Atlas Novus Pars Quarta, J. Blaeu, 1646: 11 2Y 159-160
2:302-3 Theatrum Orbis Terrarum sive Atlas Novus Pars Quarta, J. Blaeu, 1646-48: 11 2R 133-134
2:311 Le Theatre du Monde ou Nouvel Atlas, Quatriesme Partie, J. Blaeu: 11 2R 137-138
2:312 Cinquème Volume de la Geographie Blaviane, J. Blaeu, 1663-67: 11 2N 113-114
2:321 Toonneel des Aerdycks oft Nieuwe Atlas... Vierde deel, J. Blaeu, 1648: 11 2X 147-148
2:322 Toonneel des Aerdycks oft Nieuwe Atlas... Vierde deel, J. Blaeu, 1648: 11 2Q 127-128
2:331 Novus Atlas and Atlas Major (Vierter Teil), J. Blaeu, 1645-48: 11 2Z 157-158
Nuevo Atlas del Reyno de Inglaterra, J. Blaeu, 1645/48: 11 2X 145-146

References   Van der Krogt 2002 18:20.

67   [5230:1] **Wiltshire**
**WILTONIA | sive | COMITATVS | WILTONIENSIS. | Anglis |
WIL SHIRE**
In English Wiltshire
Amstelodami Apud Ioannem Ianßonium
40 x 50 cm.

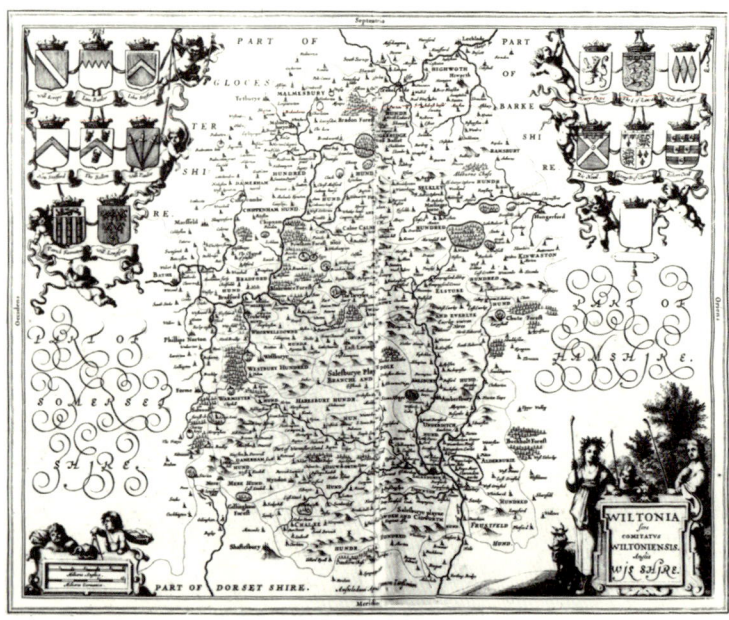

Notes   Left and right on the map are some coats of arms of particular families.

Occurrence in atlases

1:403/05 Atlas Novus, Janssonius, 1647/1657-62: v4 9 2L 113-114
1:414/15 Le Nouvel Atlas... Tome Quatrieme, Janssonius, 1646-49: v4 9 2Q 127-128
1:425 Novus Atlas, Janssonius, 1647-49: v4 9 2V 149-150
1:434/36 Nieuwen Atlas... Het Vierde deel, Janssonius, 1647-49/1658: v4 9 2M2
1:408 Atlas, Janssonius, after c. 1680: v3 8

68   [5230:2] Wiltshire
**WILTONIA | sive | COMITATVS WILTONI- | ENSIS; Anglice |
WIL SHIRE**
In English Wiltshire
41 x 50 cm.

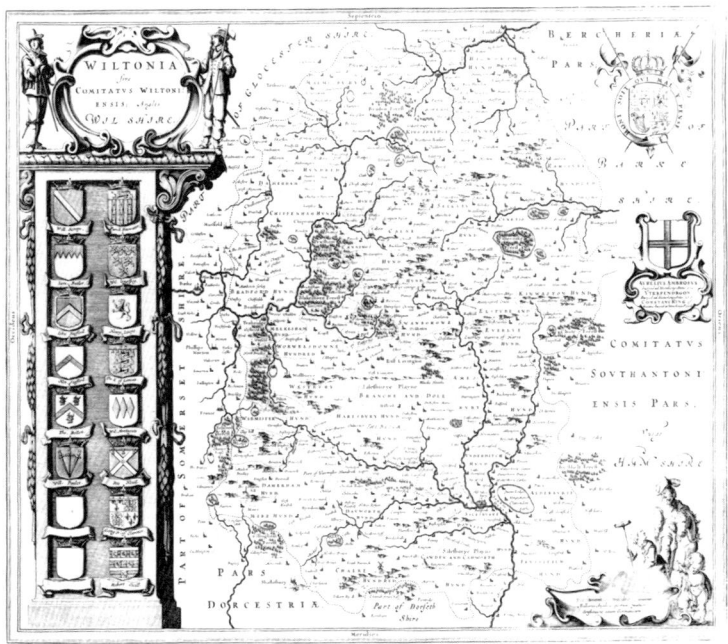

At the right of the map is the old coat of arms of England. Below it are the names
of the three kings who, according to Geoffrey of Monmouth, were buried in the
sixth century at Stonehenge: Ambrosius Aurelianus, his brother Uther Pendragon
(the father of King Arthur) and Constantine. On the left are sixteen coats of arms
of noble families of the county. The map has been copied from Speed's *Theatre*,
edition after 1623, and was specially made for the atlas of England, which Joan
Blaeu in 1645 joined as a fourth part to his *Atlas novus*.

Occurrence in atlases
2:301 Theatrum Orbis Terrarum sive Atlas Novus Pars Quarta, J. Blaeu, 1646: 8
2P 139-140
2:302-3 Theatrum Orbis Terrarum sive Atlas Novus Pars Quarta, J. Blaeu, 1646-
48: 8 2L 117-118
2:311 Le Theatre du Monde ou Nouvel Atlas, Quatriesme Partie, J. Blaeu: 8 2L
121-122
2:312 Cinquème Volume de la Geographie Blaviane, J. Blaeu, 1663-67: 8 2G
99-100
2:321 Toonneel des Aerdycks oft Nieuwe Atlas... Vierde deel, J. Blaeu, 1648: 8 2P
129-130

2:322 Toonneel des Aerdycks oft Nieuwe Atlas... Vierde deel, J. Blaeu, 1648: 8 2K 111-112

2:331 Novus Atlas and Atlas Major (Vierter Teil), J. Blaeu, 1645-48: 8 2P 137-138

Nuevo Atlas del Reyno de Inglaterra, J. Blaeu, 1645/48: 8 2O 127-128

References   Van der Krogt 2002 18:16.

69   [5230:373] Wiltshire
WILTONIA.
Wiltshire
8.5 X 12 cm.

Notes   This map is from a collection of 44 maps of the British Isles, engraved by Pieter van den Keere. The maps are comparable in size to those of the *Tabularum Geographicarum*, published by Pieter Bertius, for which Van den Keere engraved many maps. Although the maps of Van den Keere form one collection, no title-page is known.

Occurrence in atlases
373:01 Atlas of the British Isles, Van den Keere, c. 1605: 5
373:02 Britannia, Camden, 1617: 6 K iv 146

References   Skelton 1970, 4.

70.1 **[5235:1.1]** Somerset
COMITATVS | SOMERSETTENSIS. | SOMEREST-SHIRE [!]
Somerset,
38 x 50 cm.

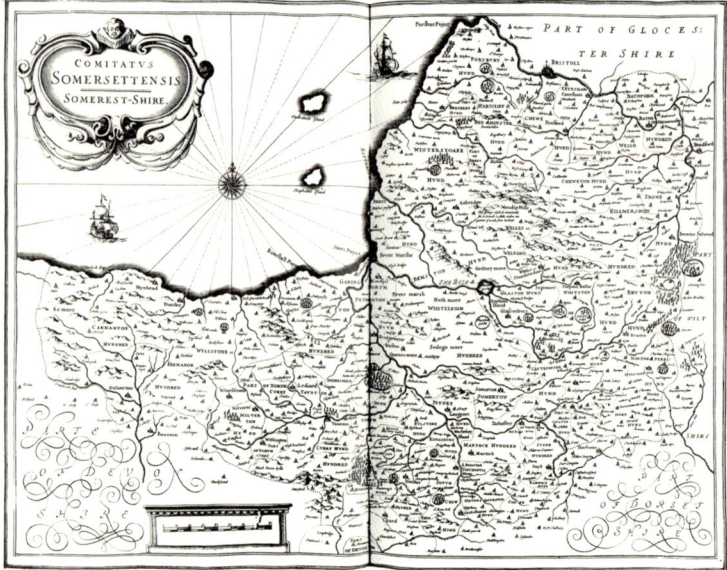

Notes The name of the county derives from Old English Sumorsǣ‾te, which is short for Sumortūnsǣ‾te, meaning 'the people living at or dependent upon Sumortūn'. *Sumortūn* is modern Somerton and may mean 'summer settlement', a farmstead occupied during the summer but abandoned in the winter. The scalebar on this map does not contain units.

Occurrence in atlases
1:324 Appendix Atlantis, Janssonius, 1636: 13 M
1:323 Newer Atlas, Janssonius, 1636: VI 21 T(M)
1:332 Appendix Atlantis, Janssonius/Hondius, 1637: 11 P
1:421/2 Newer Atlas, Janssonius, 1638: VI 16 M
1:431 Nieuwen Atlas, Janssonius, 1638-44: VI 15 V(P)

70.2 [5235:1.2] Somerset
SOMERSET- | TENSIS | COMITATVS: | Somerset Shire
Somerset
Amstelodami | apud Joannem Janßonium.

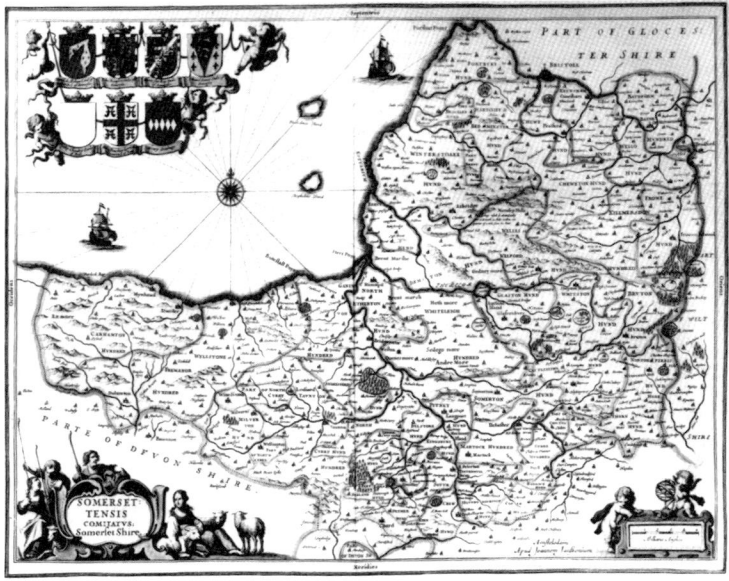

Notes On the top left there are seven coats of arms of noble families, one of which is empty.

Occurrence in atlases
1:403/05 Atlas Novus, Janssonius, 1647/1657-62: v4 10 2N 119-120
1:414/15 Le Nouvel Atlas... Tome Quatrieme, Janssonius, 1646-49: v4 10 2T 135-136
1:425 Novus Atlas, Janssonius, 1647-49: v4 10 2Z 157-158
1:434/36 Nieuwen Atlas... Het Vierde deel, Janssonius, 1647-49/1658: v4 10 2N 109-110
1:408 Atlas, Janssonius, after c. 1680: v3 9

71   [5235:2] Somerset
SOMERSET- | TENSIS | COMITATVS. | Somerset shire
Somerset
38.5 X 50 cm.

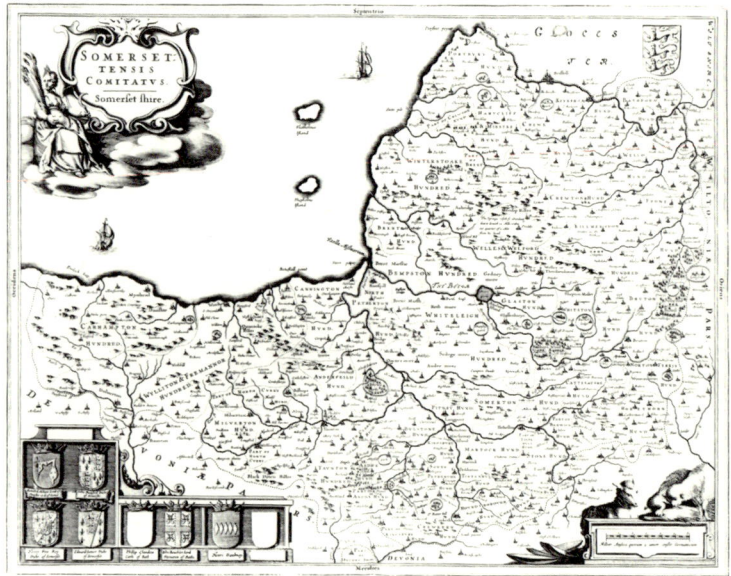

Notes   Ceres, the goddess of agriculture, is drawn in the title cartouche. The
coats of arms beneath the title cartouche are of the lords of Somerset. The map
has been copied from Speed's *Theatre*, edition after 1623, and was specially made
for the atlas of England, which Joan Blaeu in 1645 joined as a fourth part to his
Atlas novus.

Occurrence in atlases
2:301 Theatrum Orbis Terrarum sive Atlas Novus Pars Quarta, J. Blaeu, 1646: 7
2L 127-128
2:302-3 Theatrum Orbis Terrarum sive Atlas Novus Pars Quarta, J. Blaeu, 1646-
48: 7 2H 107-108
2:311 Le Theatre du Monde ou Nouvel Atlas, Quatriesme Partie, J. Blaeu: 7 2H
111-122
2:312 Cinquème Volume de la Geographie Blaviane, J. Blaeu, 1663-67: 7 2D 91-92
2:321 Toonneel des Aerdycks oft Nieuwe Atlas... Vierde deel, J. Blaeu, 1648: 7 2M
119-120
2:322 Toonneel des Aerdycks oft Nieuwe Atlas... Vierde deel, J. Blaeu, 1648: 7 2G
101-102
2:331 Novus Atlas and Atlas Major (Vierter Teil), J. Blaeu, 1645-48: 7 2L 125-126
Nuevo Atlas del Reyno de Inglaterra, J. Blaeu, 1645/48: 7 2L 117-118

References   Van der Krogt 2002 18:15.

72   [5235:373] Somerset
        Somersetia
        Somerset
        Petrus | Kærius | cælavit.
        8.5 x 12 cm.

Notes   This map is from a collection of 44 maps of the British Isles, engraved by
Pieter van den Keere. The maps are comparable in size to those of the *Tabularum*
Geographicarum, published by Pieter Bertius, for which Van den Keere engraved
many maps. Although the maps of Van den Keere form one collection, no title-
page is known.

Occurrence in atlases

373:01 Atlas of the British Isles, Van den Keere, c. 1605: 4
373:02 Britannia, Camden, 1617: 5 I3v 134

References   Skelton 1970, 4.

73   [5240:1] Dorset
COMITATVS | DORCESTRIA. | Vulgo Anglice | DORSET SHIRE
In popular speech in English Dorset
Amstelodami | apud Joannem Janßonium.
38 x 50 cm.

Notes   Left above, underneath the title cartouche, there are four coats of arms of noble families. One of them is empty.

Occurrence in atlases

1:403/05 Atlas Novus, Janssonius, 1647/1657-62: v4 11 2Q 129-130
1:414/15 Le Nouvel Atlas... Tome Quatrieme, Janssonius, 1646-49: v4 11 2Y 145-146
1:425 Novus Atlas, Janssonius, 1647-49: v4 11 3D 169-170
1:434/36 Nieuwen Atlas... Het Vierde deel, Janssonius, 1647-49/1658: v4 11 2N2
1:408 Atlas, Janssonius, after c. 1680: v3 10

74   [5240:2] Dorset
COMITATVS | DORCESTRIA, | sive | DORSETTIA; | Vulgo
Anglice | DORSET SHIRE
In popular speech in English Dorset
38 x 50 cm.

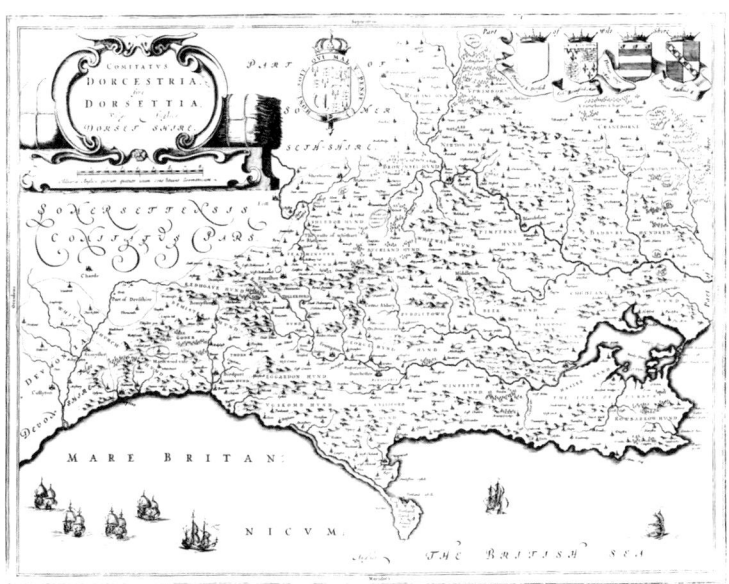

Notes   The map includes the coats of arms of the earls of Dorset. The map has
been copied from Speed's *Theatre*, edition after 1623, and was specially made for
the atlas of England, which Joan Blaeu in 1645 joined as a fourth part to his *Atlas
novus*.

Occurrence in atlases

2:301 Theatrum Orbis Terrarum sive Atlas Novus Pars Quarta, J. Blaeu, 1646: 6
2I 121-122

2:302-3 Theatrum Orbis Terrarum sive Atlas Novus Pars Quarta, J. Blaeu, 1646-
48: 6 2F 101-102

2:311 Le Theatre du Monde ou Nouvel Atlas, Quatriesme Partie, J. Blaeu: 6 2F
111-112

2:312 Cinquème Volume de la Geographie Blaviane, J. Blaeu, 1663-67: 6 2B 87-88

2:321 Toonneel des Aerdrycks oft Nieuwe Atlas... Vierde deel, J. Blaeu, 1648: 6 2K
113-114

2:322 Toonneel des Aerdrycks oft Nieuwe Atlas... Vierde deel, J. Blaeu, 1648: 6
2D 97-98

2:331 Novus Atlas and Atlas Major (Vierter Teil), J. Blaeu, 1645-48: 6 2I 119-120
Nuevo Atlas del Reyno de Inglaterra, J. Blaeu, 1645/48: 6 2I 111-112

References   Van der Krogt 2002 18:14.

75   [5240:373] Dorset

Dorcestria

Dorset

Petrus | Kærius | cælavit.

8.5 x 12 cm.

Notes   This map is from a collection of 44 maps of the British Isles, engraved by
Pieter van den Keere. The maps are comparable in size to those of the *Tabularum
Geographicarum*, published by Pieter Bertius, for which Van den Keere engraved
many maps. Although the maps of Van den Keere form one collection, no title-
page is known.

Occurrence in atlases

373:01 Atlas of the British Isles, Van den Keere, c. 1605: 3
373:02 Britannia, Camden, 1617: 4 H7r 125

References   Skelton 1970, 4.

76.1 [5250:1.1] Devon
DEVONIÆ | DESCRIPTIO. | The DESCRIPTION of | DEVON-SHIRE
Map of Devon
Amstelodami Apud Ioannem Ianßonium
38 x 48.5 cm.

Notes The cartouche is flanked by two women; one with a snake, the other with a cross. There are no coats of arms.

Occurrence in atlases
1:432 Des Nieuwen Atlantis Aenhang, Janssonius, 1644: 9 i

76.2 [5250:1.2] Devon
DEVONIÆ | DESCRIPTIO. | The DESCRIPTION of | DEVON-SHIRE
Map of Devon
Amstelodami Apud Ioannem Ianßonium

Notes At the bottom left on the map are the coats of arms of some noble families.

Occurrence in atlases
1:403/05 Atlas Novus, Janssonius, 1647/1657-62: v4 12 2S 133-134
1:414/15 Le Nouvel Atlas... Tome Quatrieme, Janssonius, 1646-49: v4 12 3A 151-152
1:425 Novus Atlas, Janssonius, 1647-49: v4 12 3F 175-176
1:434/36 Nieuwen Atlas... Het Vierde deel, Janssonius, 1647-49/1658: v4 12 2O
1:408 Atlas, Janssonius, after c. 1680: v3 11

77   [5250:2] Devon
DEVONIA | vulgo | DEVON-SHIRE
In popular speech Devon
39 x 50 cm.

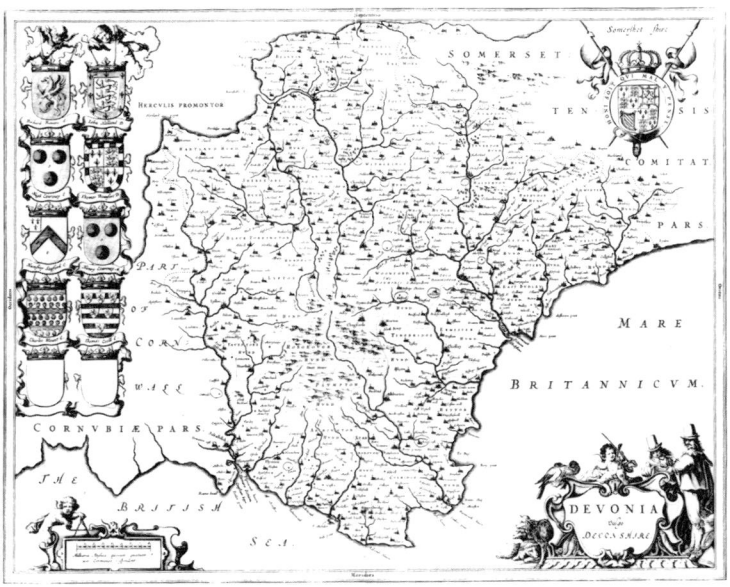

Notes   On the left are the coats of arms of the earls and dukes of Devon. The map has been copied from Speed's *Theatre*, edition after 1623, and was specially made for the atlas of England, which Joan Blaeu in 1645 joined as a fourth part to his *Atlas novus*.

Occurrence in atlases

2:301 Theatrum Orbis Terrarum sive Atlas Novus Pars Quarta, J. Blaeu, 1646: 5 2G 115-116

2:302-3 Theatrum Orbis Terrarum sive Atlas Novus Pars Quarta, J. Blaeu, 1646-48: 5 2D 95-96

2:311 Le Theatre du Monde ou Nouvel Atlas, Quatriesme Partie, J. Blaeu: 5 2D(D) 105-106

2:312 Cinquème Volume de la Geographie Blaviane, J. Blaeu, 1663-67: 5 Z 81-82

2:321 Toonneel des Aerdycks oft Nieuwe Atlas... Vierde deel, J. Blaeu, 1648: 5 2G 105-106

2:322 Toonneel des Aerdycks oft Nieuwe Atlas... Vierde deel, J. Blaeu, 1648: 5 2C 91-92

2:331 Novus Atlas and Atlas Major (Vierter Teil), J. Blaeu, 1645-48: 5 2G 113-114

Nuevo Atlas del Reyno de Inglaterra, J. Blaeu, 1645/48: 5 2G 105-106

References   Van der Krogt 2002 18:13.

78.1   [5250:352.1] Devon
DEVONIÆ | DESCRIPTIO
Map of Devon
Petrus Kærius Cælavit.
16 x 20.5 cm.

Notes   The name Devon derives from the name of the Celtic people who inhabited the southwestern peninsula of Britain at the time of the Roman invasion c. AD 50, known as the Dumnonii, thought to mean "deep valley dwellers". In the Brythonic Celtic languages, Devon is known as Dyfnaint (Welsh), Devnent in Breton and Dewnans (Cornish). William Camden, in his 1607 edition of Britannia, described Devon as being one part of an older, wider country that once included Cornwall.

Occurrence in atlases
352:32/33 Atlas Minor, Janssonius, 1648-51: vi 9 E2r 35

78.2   [5250:352.2] Devon
COMTÉ | DE | DEVON.
Devon

Notes   This map appeared in the *Atlas soulagé de son gros & pesant fardeau*, published by Pieter van der Aa. Almost all the maps are printed from reworked plates of Janssonius's *Atlas Minor*. The titles and scale were translated into French. Several Latin texts on the maps have been removed, as have the Latin names of the wind directions in the borders. The cartouches have been modernized and windroses added. Other modernizations are the removal of ships and sea monsters, and erasing names in curled letters and replacing them with Roman type letters. Latin names of seas and countries are often translated into French.

Occurrence in atlases
352:51.2-9 Atlas soulagé..., Van der Aa, c. 1714: v4 4 blank

79 [5250:373] Devon
DEVONIA
Devon
P. Kærius | cælavit.
8.5 x 12 cm.

Notes This map is from a collection of 44 maps of the British Isles, engraved by
Pieter van den Keere. The maps are comparable in size to those of the *Tabularum
Geographicarum*, published by Pieter Bertius, for which Van den Keere engraved
many maps. Although the maps of Van den Keere form one collection, no title-
page is known.

Occurrence in atlases
373:01 Atlas of the British Isles, Van den Keere, c. 1605: 2
373:02 Britannia, Camden, 1617: 3 H1r 113

References Skelton 1970, 4.

80   [5255:1] Cornwall
CORNUBIA | sive | CORNWALLIA
Cornwall
Amstelodami Excudebat Ioannes Ianßonius
38 X 51 cm.

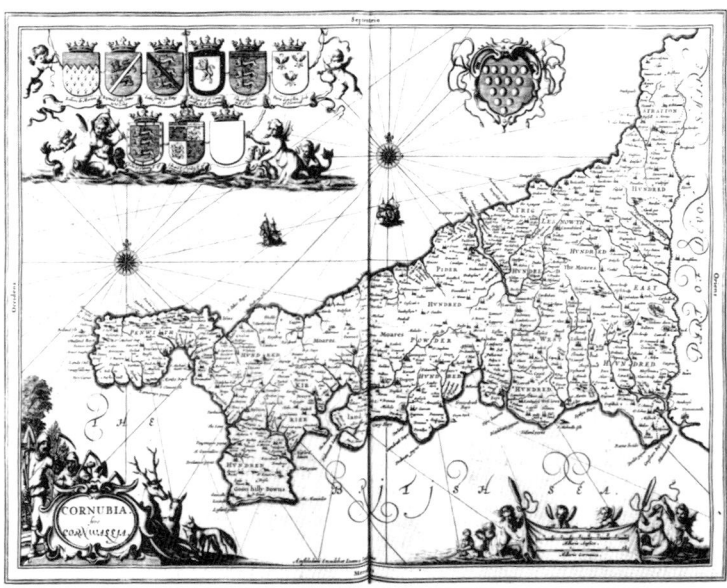

Notes   This map of Cornwall has a figurative cartouche and scale of miles, ten coats of arms, images of sailing ships and two compass roses. At the top right is the banner of the Duchy of Cornwall, one of the two royal duchies in England.

Occurrence in atlases
1:403/05 Atlas Novus, Janssonius, 1647/1657-62: v4 13 2V 138-139
1:414/15 Le Nouvel Atlas... Tome Quatrieme, Janssonius, 1646-49: v4 13 3C 157-158
1:425 Novus Atlas, Janssonius, 1647-49: v4 13 3H 181-182
1:434/36 Nieuwen Atlas... Het Vierde deel, Janssonius, 1647-49/1658: v4 13 2P 113-114
1:408 Atlas, Janssonius, after c. 1680: v3 12

81   [5255:2] Cornwall
      CORNVBIA | sive | CORNWALLIA
      Cornwall
      39 x 50 cm.

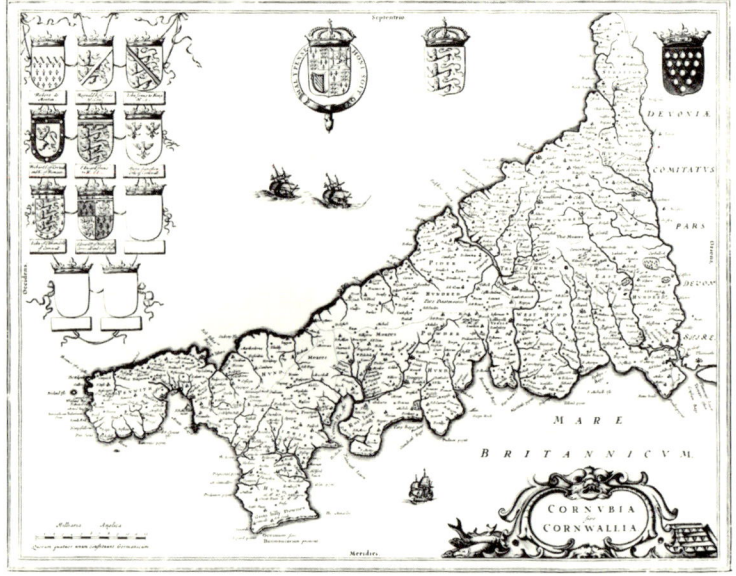

Notes   On the left is the coats of arms of the earls of Cornwall and along the top edge the royal coat of arms and the coats of arms of England and Cornwall. The title cartouche is flanked by images of fish and tin, products of Cornwall.

Occurrence in atlases
2:301 Theatrum Orbis Terrarum sive Atlas Novus Pars Quarta, J. Blaeu, 1646: 4 2D 103-106
2:302-3 Theatrum Orbis Terrarum sive Atlas Novus Pars Quarta, J. Blaeu, 1646-48: 4 2A 87-88
2:311 Le Theatre du Monde ou Nouvel Atlas, Quatriesme Partie, J. Blaeu: 4 2A 97-98
2:312 Cinquème Volume de la Geographie Blaviane, J. Blaeu, 1663-67: 4 X 75-76
2:321 Toonneel des Aerdrycks oft Nieuwe Atlas... Vierde deel, J. Blaeu, 1648: 4 2E 99-100
2:322 Toonneel des Aerdrycks oft Nieuwe Atlas... Vierde deel, J. Blaeu, 1648: 4 Z 83-84
2:331 Novus Atlas and Atlas Major (Vierter Teil), J. Blaeu, 1645-48: 4 2D 103-104
Nuevo Atlas del Reyno de Inglaterra, J. Blaeu, 1645/48: 4 2D 95-96

References   Van der Krogt 2002 18:12.

82   [5255:341(Wright)] Cornwall
Promontorium Angliæ | Cornubia. Iuxta quod | genuina hicdatur
Situatio | Insularum Sorlingarum | adquas multæ illidunt | naves
Cornwall, peninsula of England with the real location of the Scilly
Islands on whose coasts many ships have floundered.
Ben. W. cælator.
8.5 x 12 cm.

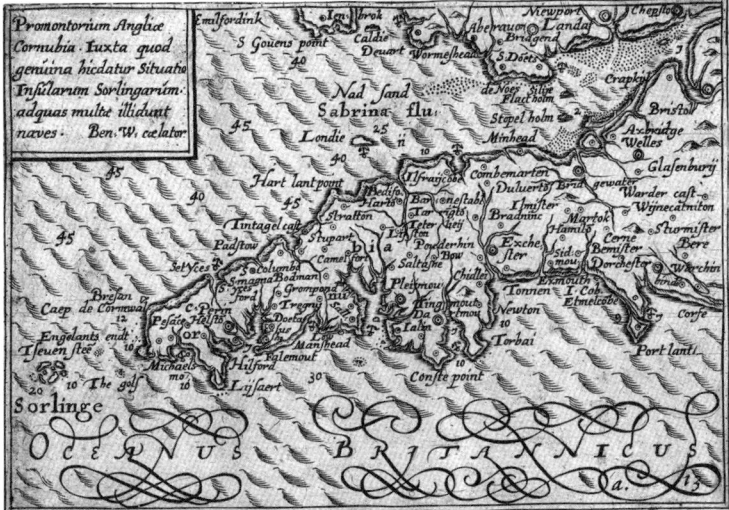

Notes   The name Cornwall comes from combining two different terms from
separate languages. The Roman term for the Celtic tribe which inhabited what is
now Cornwall at the time of Roman rule in Britain, Cornovii, came from a Brythonic tribal name which gave modern Cornish Kernow, also known as Corneu to
the Brythons. This could be from either of two sources; the common Celtic root
cern, or the Latin cornu, both of which mean "horn" or "peninsula", suggestive of
the shape of Cornwall's landmass.

Occurrence in atlases
341:54 Tabulae Geographicae Contractae, C.J. Visscher, 1649: 12 a.13

83   [5255:373] Cornwall
Cornuwallia.
Cornwall
8.5 x 12 cm.

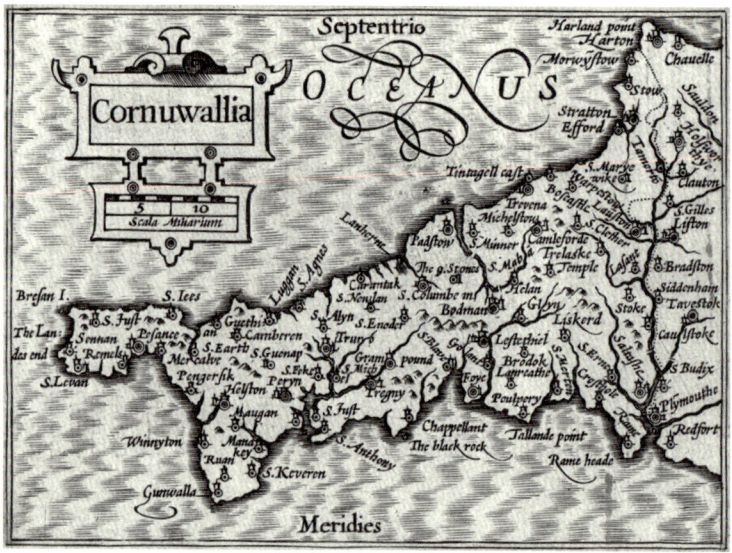

Notes   This map is from a collection of 44 maps of the British Isles, engraved by Pieter van den Keere. The maps are comparable in size to those of the *Tabularum Geographicarum*, published by Pieter Bertius, for which Van den Keere engraved many maps. Although the maps of Van den Keere form one collection, no title-page is known.

Occurrence in atlases

373:01 Atlas of the British Isles, Van den Keere, c. 1605: 1
373:02 Britannia, Camden, 1617: 2 G3r 101

References   Skelton 1970, 4.

84   [5260:1] Gloucestershire
GLOCESTRIA | DVCATVS, cum | MONVMETHENSI |
Comitatu. | GLOCESTER SHIRE | & MONMOUTH SHIRE
The duchy of Gloucester with the county of Monmouth. Gloucestershire and Monmouthshire
41 X 51 cm.

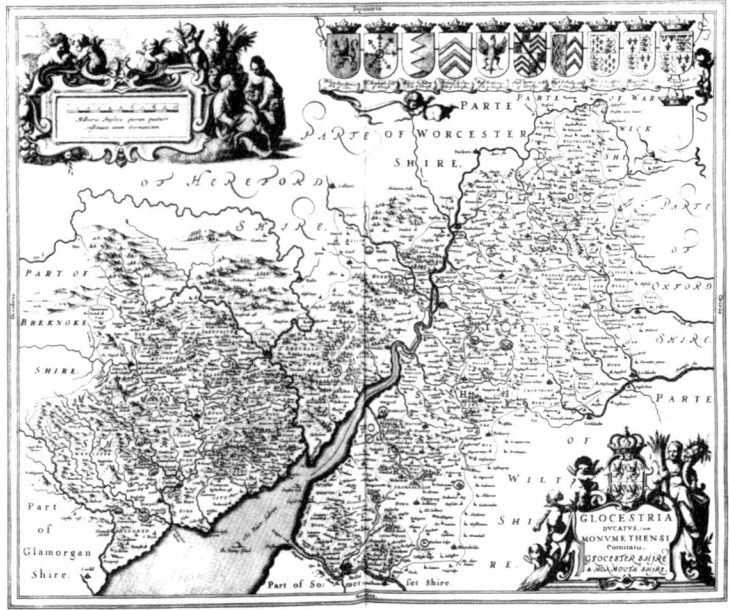

Notes   At the top right there are ten coats of arms of noble families.

Occurrence in atlases
1:403/05 Atlas Novus, Janssonius, 1647/1657-62: v4 14 2Y 145-146
1:414/15 Le Nouvel Atlas... Tome Quatrieme, Janssonius, 1646-49: v4 14 3E 163-
164
1:425 Novus Atlas, Janssonius, 1647-49: v4 14 3L 191-192
1:434/36 Nieuwen Atlas... Het Vierde deel, Janssonius, 1647-49/1658: v4 14 2Q
115-116
1:408 Atlas, Janssonius, after c. 1680: v3 13

85   [5260:2] Gloucestershire
       GLOCESTRIA | DVCATVS; | Vulgo | GLOCESTER | SHIRE
       The duchy of Gloucester, in the vulgar tongue Gloucestershire
       41 x 50 cm.

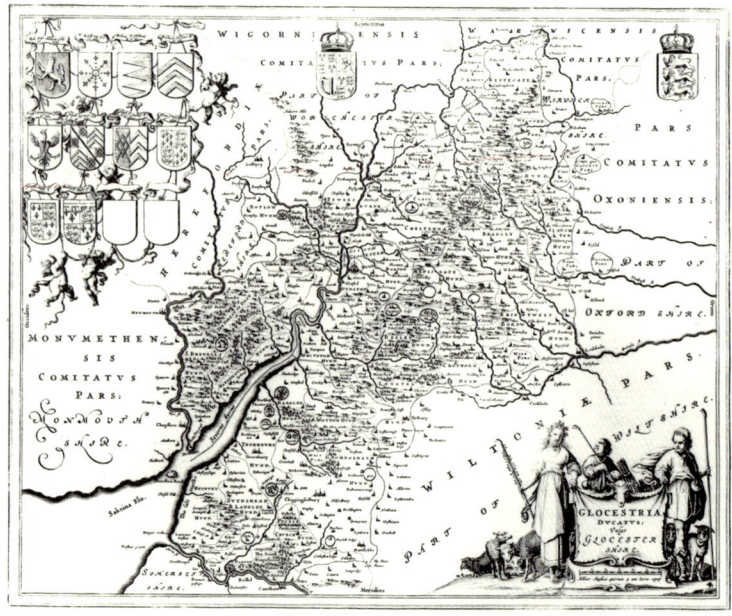

Notes   The title has been placed on a sheep skin, held by a shepherd and shep-
herdess. Above stand the coats of arms of the earls and dukes of Gloucester. The
map has been copied from Speed's *Theatre*, edition after 1623, and was specially
made for the atlas of England, which Joan Blaeu in 1645 joined as a fourth part
to his *Atlas novus*.

Occurrence in atlases
2:301 Theatrum Orbis Terrarum sive Atlas Novus Pars Quarta, J. Blaeu, 1646: 15
3M 197-198
2:302-3 Theatrum Orbis Terrarum sive Atlas Novus Pars Quarta, J. Blaeu, 1646-
48: 15 3F 167-168
2:311 Le Theatre du Monde ou Nouvel Atlas, Quatriesme Partie, J. Blaeu: 15 3E 171-172
2:312 Cinquème Volume de la Geographie Blaviane, J. Blaeu, 1663-67: 15 3A 143-144
2:321 Toonneel des Aerdycks oft Nieuwe Atlas... Vierde deel, J. Blaeu, 1648: 15
3K 183-184
2:322 Toonneel des Aerdycks oft Nieuwe Atlas... Vierde deel, J. Blaeu, 1648: 15
3B 157-158
2:331 Novus Atlas and Atlas Major (Vierter Teil), J. Blaeu, 1645-48: 15 3M 193-194
Nuevo Atlas del Reyno de Inglaterra, J. Blaeu, 1645/48: 15 3K 179-180

References   Van der Krogt 2002 18:26.

86   [5260:373] **Gloucestershire**
Glocestria.
Gloucestershire
8.5 X 12.5 cm.

Notes   This map is from a collection of 44 maps of the British Isles, engraved by
Pieter van den Keere. The maps are comparable in size to those of the *Tabularum
Geographicarum*, published by Pieter Bertius, for which Van den Keere engraved
many maps. Although the maps of Van den Keere form one collection, no title-
page is known.

Occurrence in atlases
373:01 Atlas of the British Isles, Van den Keere, c. 1605: 7
373:02 Britannia, Camden, 1617: 9 O5r 217

References   Skelton 1970, 4.

87.1 [5265:1.1] Oxfordshire
PROVINCIA | OXONIENSIS | OXFORD-SHIRE
Oxfordshire
Apud Ioannem Ianßonium
38 x 48 cm.

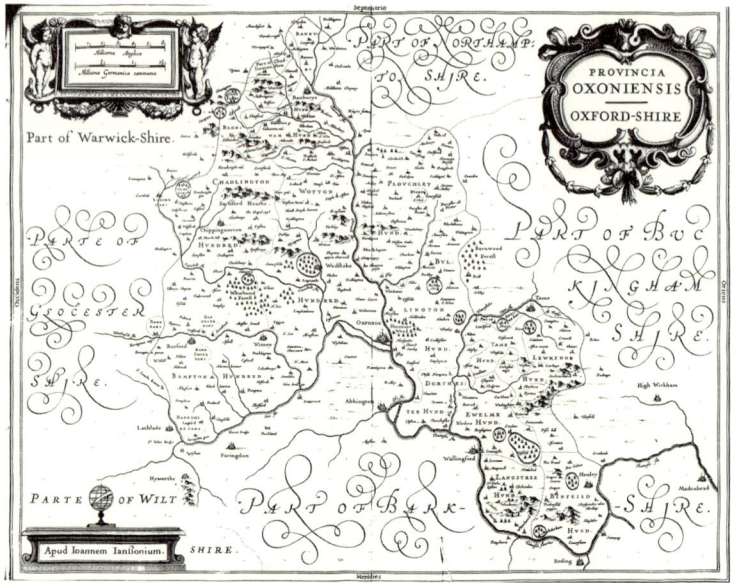

Notes Oxfordshire was formed in the early years of the tenth century and is broadly situated in the land between the River Thames to the south, the Cotswolds to the west, the Chilterns to the east and the Midlands to the north, with spurs running south to Henley-on-Thames and north to Banbury.

Occurrence in atlases
1:432 Des Nieuwen Atlantis Aenhang, Janssonius, 1644: 3 c
1:434/36 Nieuwen Atlas... Het Vierde deel, Janssonius, 1647-49/1658: v4 15 2S

87.2   [5265:1.2] Oxfordshire
OXONIUM | Comitatus | Vulgo | OXFORD | SHIRE
The county of Oxford, in the vulgar tongue Oxfordshire

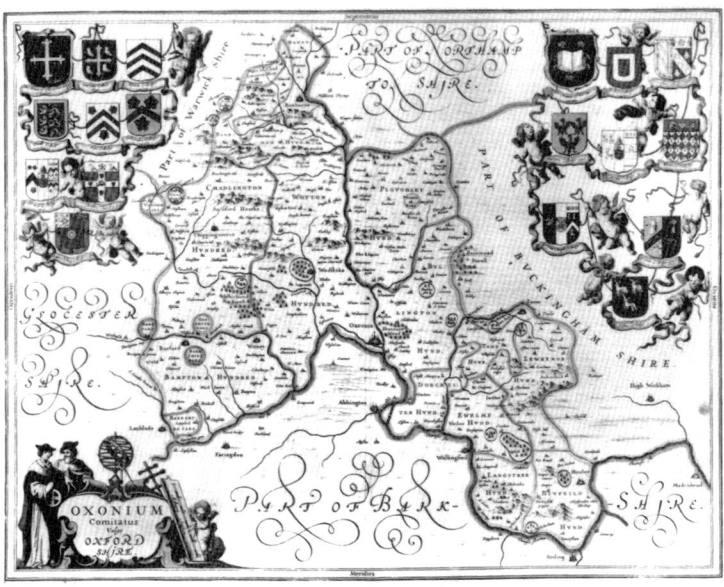

Notes   At the bottom left is the title cartouche, with an image of a sphere and two scientists; a total of 18 coats of arms appear the top corners.

Occurrence in atlases

1:403/05 Atlas Novus, Janssonius, 1647/1657-62: v4 15 3B 155-156
1:414/15 Le Nouvel Atlas... Tome Quatrieme, Janssonius, 1646-49: v4 15 3I 175-176
1:425 Novus Atlas, Janssonius, 1647-49: v4 15 3P 203-204
1:434/36 Nicuwen Atlas... Het Vierde deel, Janssonius, 1647-49/1658: v4 15 2S
1:408 Atlas, Janssonius, after c. 1680: v3 14

88   [5265:2] Oxfordshire
OXONIVM | Comitatus, Vulgo | OXFORD SHIRE
The county of Oxford, in the vulgar tongue Oxfordshire
Ioh. Blaeu excud.
38 x 50 cm.

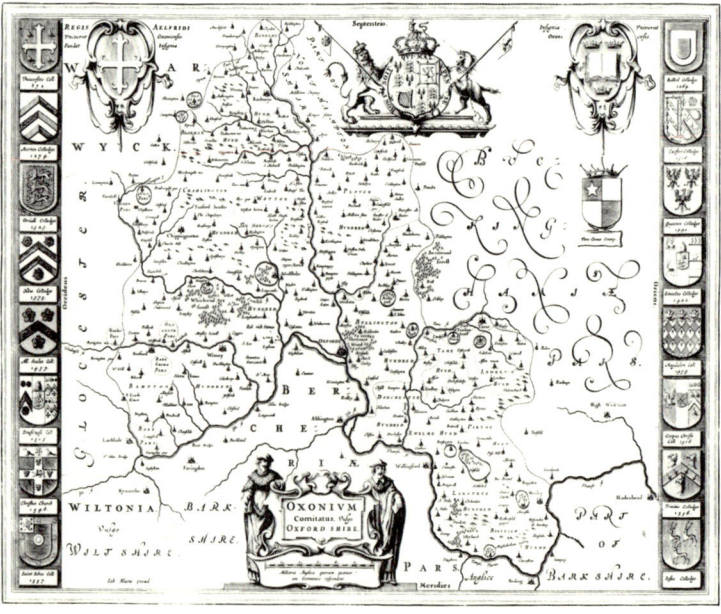

Notes   At the top left is the coat of arms of King Alfred, the claimed founder of
the University of Oxford. At the top right is the coat of arms of the University of
Oxford, and below that is the coat of arms of the de Vere earls of Oxford. The coats
of arms around the edges of the map are those of the colleges of the university, each
with its name and foundation date (for Jesus College the foundation date of 1571
is lacking). The map has been copied from Speed's *Theatre*, edition after 1623, and
was specially made for the atlas of England, which Joan Blaeu in 1645 joined as a
fourth part to his *Atlas novus*.

Occurrence in atlases
2:301 Theatrum Orbis Terrarum sive Atlas Novus Pars Quarta, J. Blaeu, 1646: 16
3G 205-206
2:302-3 Theatrum Orbis Terrarum sive Atlas Novus Pars Quarta, J. Blaeu, 1646-
48: 16 3H 173-174
2:311 Le Theatre du Monde ou Nouvel Atlas, Quatriesme Partie, J. Blaeu: 16 3G
177-178
2:312 Cinquème Volume de la Geographie Blaviane, J. Blaeu, 1663-67: 16 3c 149-
150
2:321 Toonneel des Aerdycks oft Nieuwe Atlas... Vierde deel, J. Blaeu, 1648: 16
3N 193-194

2:322 Toonneel des Aerdycks oft Nieuwe Atlas... Vierde deel, J. Blaeu, 1648: 16
3D 163-164

2:331 Novus Atlas and Atlas Major (Vierter Teil), J. Blaeu, 1645-48: 16 3P 201-
202

Nuevo Atlas del Reyno de Inglaterra, J. Blaeu, 1645/48: 16 3M 185-186

References   Van der Krogt 2002 18:27.

89.1   [5265:352.1] Oxfordshire
OXONIENSIS | COMITATVS | DESCRIPTIO.
Map of Oxfordshire
14.5 x 20 cm.

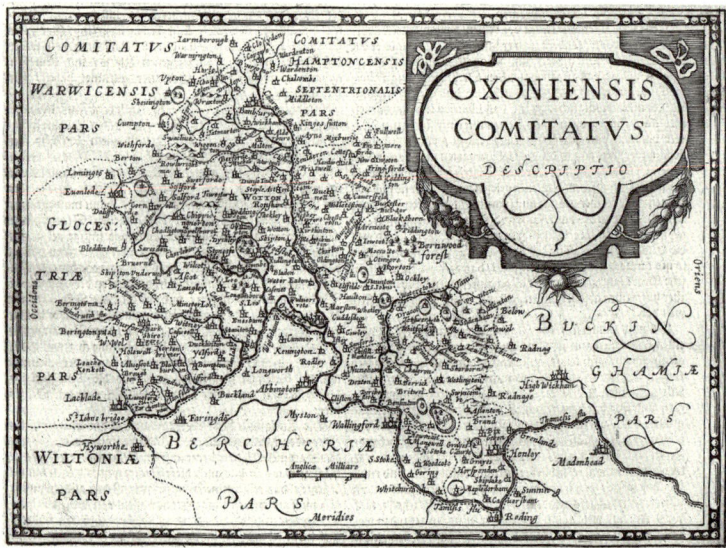

Notes   Historically this area has always had some importance, containing valuable agricultural land in the centre of the country and the prestigious university in the county town of Oxford (whose name is derived from Anglo-Saxon *Oxenaford* = "ford for oxen").

Occurrence in atlases

352:32/33 Atlas Minor, Janssonius, 1648-51: VI 16 H4r 63

89.2   [5265:352.2] Oxfordshire
LE COMTÉ | D'OXFORD.
Oxfordshire

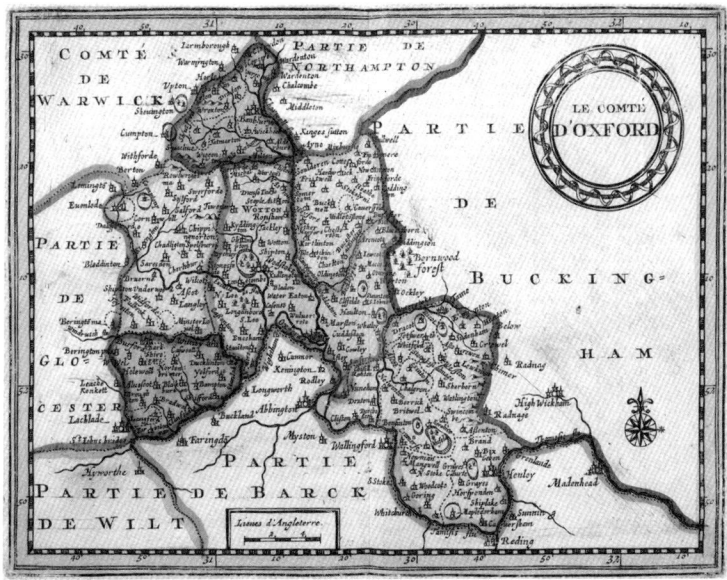

Notes   This map appeared in the *Atlas soulagé de son gros & pesant fardeau*, published by Pieter van der Aa. Almost all the maps are printed from reworked plates of Janssonius's *Atlas Minor*. The titles and scale were translated into French. Several Latin texts on the maps have been removed, as have the Latin names of the wind directions in the borders. The cartouches have been modernized and windroses added. Other modernizations are the removal of ships and sea monsters, and erasing names in curled letters and replacing them with Roman type letters. Latin names of seas and countries are often translated into French.

Occurrence in atlases
352:51.2-9 Atlas soulagé..., Van der Aa, c. 1714: v4 6 blank

90   [5265:373] Oxfordshire, Buckinghamshire and Berkshire
      Oxonij Buckin- | ghamiæ & Ber- | ceriæ comita- | tum descriptio
      Map of the counties Oxfordshire, Buckinghamshire and Berkshire.
      Petrus Kærius | cælavit.
      8.5 x 12 cm.

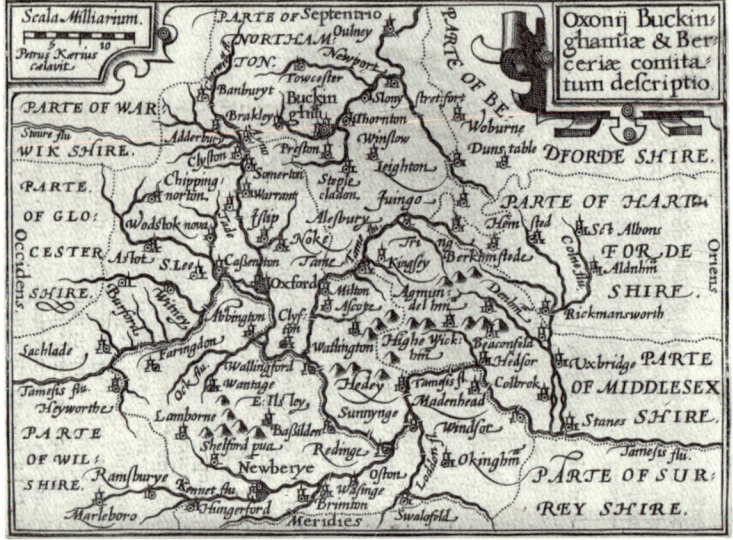

Notes   This map is from a collection of 44 maps of the British Isles, engraved by
Pieter van den Keere. The maps are comparable in size to those of the *Tabularum
Geographicarum*, published by Pieter Bertius, for which Van den Keere engraved
many maps. Although the maps of Van den Keere form one collection, no title-
page is known.

Occurrence in atlases
373:01 Atlas of the British Isles, Van den Keere, c. 1605: 8
373:02 Britannia, Camden, 1617: 10 P1r 225

References   Skelton 1970, 4.

91   [5270:1] Bedfordshire and Buckinghamshire
BUCKINGHAMIÆ | COMITATVS | cum BEDFORDIENSI; |
vulgo | BUCKINGHAMSHIRE | and | BEDFORDSHIRE
Buckinghamshire with Bedfordshire, in popular speech the County
of Buckingham
Amstelodami | apud Joannem Janßonium.
40.5 X 50.5 cm.

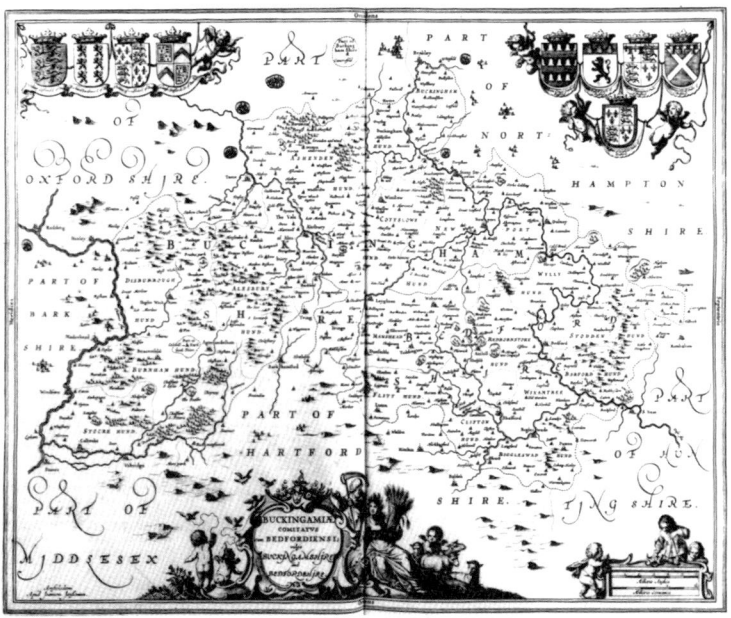

Notes   Left and right on the map are the coats of arms of some noble families.

Occurrence in atlases

1:403/05 Atlas Novus, Janssonius, 1647/1657-62: v4 16 3D 161-162
1:414/15 Le Nouvel Atlas... Tome Quatrieme, Janssonius, 1646-49: v4 16 3M 183-184
1:425 Novus Atlas, Janssonius, 1647-49: v4 16 3S 211-212
1:434/36 Nieuwen Atlas... Het Vierde deel, Janssonius, 1647-49/1658: v4 16 2S2
1:408 Atlas, Janssonius, after c. 1680: v3 15

92 + 93 [5270+5271:2] Bedfordshire and Buckinghamshire
**BEDFORDIENSIS | COMITATVS, | Anglis | BEDFORD SHIRE;
[right] BVCKINGHAMI- | ENSIS COMITATVS, | Anglis | BUCK-
INGHAM SHIRE**
In English Bedfordshire;In English Buckinghamshire
42 X 51.5 cm.

Notes   On the left of the map are the coats of arms of the earls of Bedford and
on the right of the map those of the earls and dukes of Buckingham. The two maps
appear on one copperplate, specially made for the atlas of England, which Joan
Blaeu in 1645 joined as a fourth part to his *Atlas novus*. The maps have been copied
from Speed's *Theatre*, edition after 1623.

Occurrence in atlases   2:301 Theatrum Orbis Terrarum sive Atlas Novus Pars
     Quarta, J. Blaeu, 1646: 17 3S 213-214
2:302-3 Theatrum Orbis Terrarum sive Atlas Novus Pars Quarta, J. Blaeu, 1646-
48: 17 3L 181-182
2:311 Le Theatre du Monde ou Nouvel Atlas, Quatriesme Partie, J. Blaeu: 17 3K 185-186
2:312 Cinquème Volume de la Geographie Blaviane, J. Blaeu, 1663-67: 17 3E 155-156
2:321 Toonneel des Aerdycks oft Nieuwe Atlas... Vierde deel, J. Blaeu, 1648: 17
3Q 201-202
2:322 Toonneel des Aerdycks oft Nieuwe Atlas... Vierde deel, J. Blaeu, 1648: 17
3G 171-172
2:331 Novus Atlas and Atlas Major (Vierter Teil), J. Blaeu, 1645-48: 17 3S 209-210
Nuevo Atlas del Reyno de Inglaterra, J. Blaeu, 1645/48: 17 3P 193-194

References   Van der Krogt 2002 18:29.

94   [5280:1] Middlesex etc.
MIDDELSEXIÆ cum | HERTFORDIÆ | COMITATU: | Midlesex
& Hertford | Shire
Middlesex with Hertfordshire
Amstelodami | apud Joannem Janßonium.
43.5 X 55 cm.

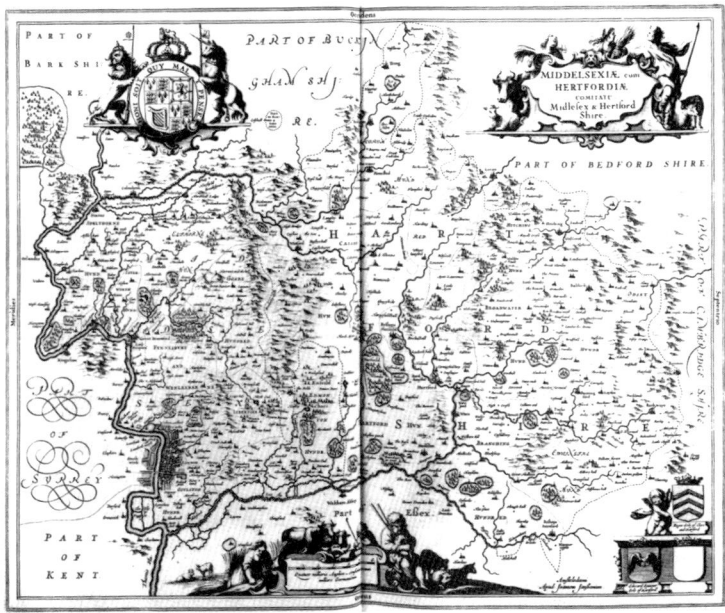

Notes   Above right is the royal coat of arms. The motto in the coat of arms is:
Honi soit qui mal y pense, which means 'Shame be to him who thinks evil of it',
the motto of the Order of the Garter.

Occurrence in atlases

1:403/05 Atlas Novus, Janssonius, 1647/1657-62: v4 17 3F 167-168
1:414/15 Le Nouvel Atlas... Tome Quatrieme, Janssonius, 1646-49: v4 17 3O 187-
188
1:425 Novus Atlas, Janssonius, 1647-49: v4 17 3V 217-218
1:434/36 Nieuwen Atlas... Het Vierde deel, Janssonius, 1647-49/1658: v4 17 2T
121-122
1:407 Atlas Contractus, Janssonius, 1666: v1 77
1:408 Atlas, Janssonius, after c. 1680: v3 16

95   [5281:2] Middlesex
MIDDLE-SEXIA
Middlesex
38 x 40.5 cm.

Notes   The image of the city London and Westminster on this map is very in-
teresting. To the left of the city we see Hyde Park and Knightsbridge. The map
has been copied from Speed's *Theatre*, edition after 1623, and was specially made
for the atlas of England, which Joan Blaeu in 1645 joined as a fourth part to his
Atlas novus.

Occurrence in atlases

2:301 Theatrum Orbis Terrarum sive Atlas Novus Pars Quarta, J. Blaeu, 1646: 19
3Z 227-228

2:302-3 Theatrum Orbis Terrarum sive Atlas Novus Pars Quarta, J. Blaeu, 1646-
48: 19 3P 193-194

2:311 Le Theatre du Monde ou Nouvel Atlas, Quatriesme Partie, J. Blaeu: 19 3O
197-198

2:312 Cinquème Volume de la Geographie Blaviane, J. Blaeu, 1663-67: 19 3I
165-166

2:321 Toonneel des Aerdycks oft Nieuwe Atlas... Vierde deel, J. Blaeu, 1648: 19
3V 213-214

2:322 Toonneel des Aerdycks oft Nieuwe Atlas... Vierde deel, J. Blaeu, 1648: 19 3L 183-184

2:331 Novus Atlas and Atlas Major (Vierter Teil), J. Blaeu, 1645-48: 19 3Z 221-222

Nuevo Atlas del Reyno de Inglaterra, J. Blaeu, 1645/48: 19 3T 205-206

References   Van der Krogt 2002 18:31.

96   [5282:2] Hertfordshire
HERTFORDIA | COMITATVS. | Vernacule | HERTFORDSHIRE
In the vernacular Hertfordshire
38 x 50 cm.

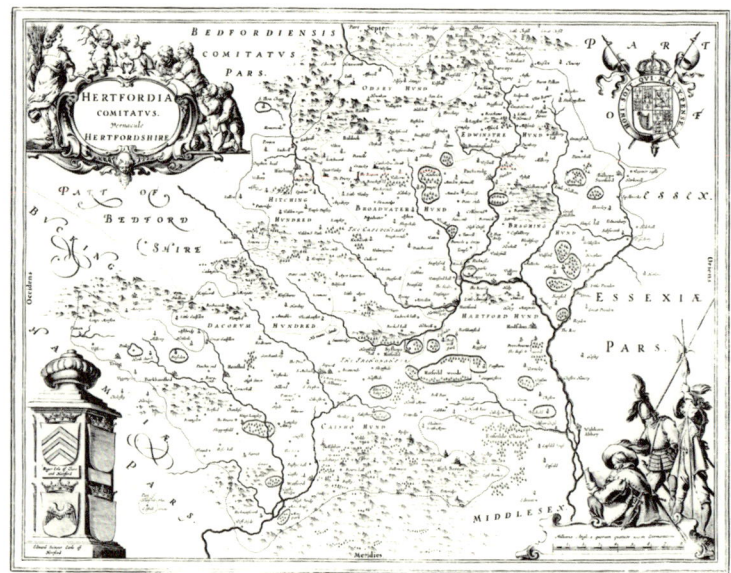

Notes   On a base stand the coats of arms of the earls of Hertford. At the scale bar
are images of three armed men, of which the sitting character draws a map. The
map has been copied from Speed's *Theatre*, edition after 1623, and was specially
made for the atlas of England, which Joan Blaeu in 1645 joined as a fourth part
to his *Atlas novus*.

Occurrence in atlases
2:301 Theatrum Orbis Terrarum sive Atlas Novus Pars Quarta, J. Blaeu, 1646: 18
3V 219-220
2:302-3 Theatrum Orbis Terrarum sive Atlas Novus Pars Quarta, J. Blaeu, 1646-
48: 18 3N 187-188
2:311 Le Theatre du Monde ou Nouvel Atlas, Quatriesme Partie, J. Blaeu: 18 3M
191-192
2:312 Cinquème Volume de la Geographie Blaviane, J. Blaeu, 1663-67: 18 3G 161-162
2:321 Toonneel des Aerdycks oft Nieuwe Atlas... Vierde deel, J. Blaeu, 1648: 18
3S 207-208
2:322 Toonneel des Aerdycks oft Nieuwe Atlas... Vierde deel, J. Blaeu, 1648: 18
3I 177-178
2:331 Novus Atlas and Atlas Major (Vierter Teil), J. Blaeu, 1645-48: 18 3X 215-216
Nuevo Atlas del Reyno de Inglaterra, J. Blaeu, 1645/48: 18 3R 199-200

References   Van der Krogt 2002 18:30.

97   [5282:373] **Hertfordshire**
Hartfordia | Comitatus.
The county of Hertford
8.5 x 12 cm.

Notes   This map is from a collection of 44 maps of the British Isles, engraved by
Pieter van den Keere. The maps are comparable in size to those of the *Tabularum
Geographicarum*, published by Pieter Bertius, for which Van den Keere engraved
many maps. Although the maps of Van den Keere form one collection, no title-
page is known.

Occurrence in atlases

373:01 Atlas of the British Isles, Van den Keere, c. 1605: 11
373:02 Britannia, Camden, 1617: 11 Q3r 245

References   Skelton 1970, 4.

98.1   [5285:1.1] Essex
ESSEXIÆ | DESCRIPTIO. | The DESCRIPTION of | ESSEX
Map of Essex
AMSTELODAMI, | Sumptibus Ioannis Ianßonii
38 x 49 cm.

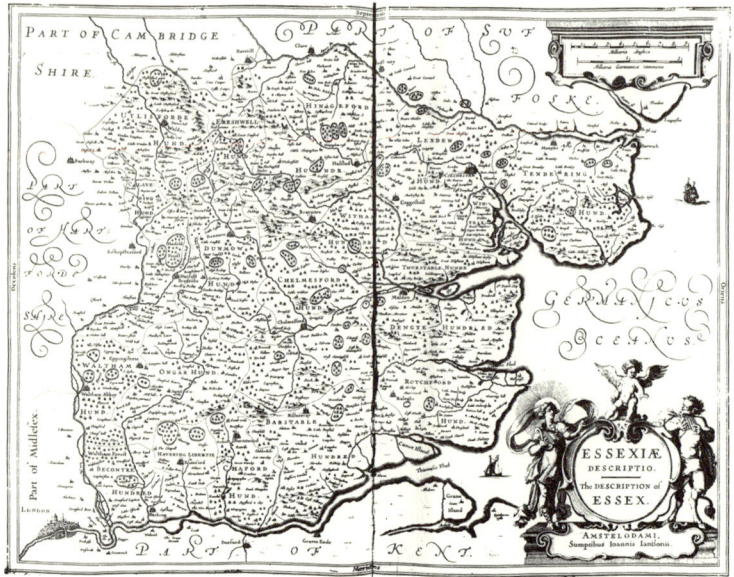

Notes   The name Essex originates in the Anglo-Saxon period and has its root in the Old English *Éastseaxe* (i.e. the East Saxons), the eastern kingdom of the Saxons.

Occurrence in atlases

1:324 Appendix Atlantis, Janssonius, 1636: 14 N
1:323 Newer Atlas, Janssonius, 1636: vi 24 Y(N)
1:332 Appendix Atlantis, Janssonius/Hondius, 1637: 12 Q(2H)
1:421/2 Newer Atlas, Janssonius, 1638: vi 17 N
1:431 Nieuwen Atlas, Janssonius, 1638-44: vi 16 X(Q)

98.2   [5285:1.2] Essex
ESSEXIÆ | DESCRIPTIO. | The DESCRIPTION of | ESSEX
Map of Essex
AMSTELODAMI, | Sumptibus Ioannis Ianßonii

Notes   This second state of the Janssonius map of Essex contains seven coats of
arms of noble families.

Occurrence in atlases

1:403/05 Atlas Novus, Janssonius, 1647/1657-62: v4 18 3K 179-180

1:414/15 Le Nouvel Atlas... Tome Quatrieme, Janssonius, 1646-49: v4 18 3T 203-
204

1:425 Novus Atlas, Janssonius, 1647-49: v4 18 4B 235-236

1:434/36 Nieuwen Atlas... Het Vierde deel, Janssonius, 1647-49/1658: v4 18 2W
127-128

1:407 Atlas Contractus, Janssonius, 1666: v1 78

1:408 Atlas, Janssonius, after c. 1680: v3 17

99   [5285:2] Essex
ESSEXIA | COMITATVS
The County of Essex
41.5 X 51.5 cm.

Notes   On the left are coats of arms of the noble families of Essex. The map has been copied from Speed's *Theatre*, edition after 1623, and was specially made for the atlas of England, which Joan Blaeu in 1645 joined as a fourth part to his *Atlas novus*.

Occurrence in atlases

2:301 Theatrum Orbis Terrarum sive Atlas Novus Pars Quarta, J. Blaeu, 1646: 20 4C 237-238

2:302-3 Theatrum Orbis Terrarum sive Atlas Novus Pars Quarta, J. Blaeu, 1646-48: 20 3S 203-204

2:311 Le Theatre du Monde ou Nouvel Atlas, Quatriesme Partie, J. Blaeu: 20 3R 107-208

2:312 Cinquème Volume de la Geographie Blaviane, J. Blaeu, 1663-67: 20 3M 175-176

2:321 Toonneel des Aerdycks oft Nieuwe Atlas... Vierde deel, J. Blaeu, 1648: 20 3Z 223-224

2:322 Toonneel des Aerdycks oft Nieuwe Atlas... Vierde deel, J. Blaeu, 1648: 20 3O 193-194

2:331 Novus Atlas and Atlas Major (Vierter Teil), J. Blaeu, 1645-48: 20 4D 233-234

Nuevo Atlas del Reyno de Inglaterra, J. Blaeu, 1645/48: 20 3Y 215-216

References   Van der Krogt 2002 18:32.

100.1   [5285:352.1] Essex
ESSEXIÆ | DESCRIPTIO
Map of Essex
Pe. Kærius | Cælavit.
16 X 20.5 cm.

Notes   In pre-Roman Britain the territories of Suffolk and Essex were home to the Trinovantes tribe, which had grown wealthy through intensive trade with the Roman Empire, contemporary to the decline of Atlantic sea trade as roads and better in-land trade-routes were established in Romanized Gaul. Catuvellaunian and Trinovantian territory was the first to be annexed by the Roman Emperor Claudius in AD 43 when he began his invasion of Britain (Cunliffe, 2001). Colchester was the capital of the province of Britannia, but was attacked and destroyed during Boudica's rebellion in AD 61. Sometime after the destruction, London became the capital of the province of Britannia.

Occurrence in atlases
352:32/33 Atlas Minor, Janssonius, 1648-51: VI 18 I4r 71

100.2 [5285:352.2] Essex
LE COMTÉ | D'ESSEX.
The county of Essex

Notes   This map appeared in the *Atlas soulagé de son gros & pesant fardeau*, published by Pieter van der Aa. Almost all the maps are printed from reworked plates of Janssonius's *Atlas Minor*. The titles and scale were translated into French. Several Latin texts on the maps have been removed, as have the Latin names of the wind directions in the borders. The cartouches have been modernized and windroses added. Other modernizations are the removal of ships and sea monsters, and erasing names in curled letters and replacing them with Roman type letters. Latin names of seas and countries are often translated into French.

Occurrence in atlases
352:51.2-9 Atlas soulagé..., Van der Aa, c. 1714: v4 7 blank

101   [5285:373] Essex
ESSEXIÆ | COMITAT.
The County of Essex
8.5 x 12 cm.

Notes   This map is from a collection of 44 maps of the British Isles, engraved by
Pieter van den Keere. The maps are comparable in size to those of the *Tabularum
Geographicarum*, published by Pieter Bertius, for which Van den Keere engraved
many maps. Although the maps of Van den Keere form one collection, no title-
page is known.

Occurrence in atlases
373:01 Atlas of the British Isles, Van den Keere, c. 1605: 12
373:02 Britannia, Camden, 1617: 12 R7v 270

References   Skelton 1970, 4.

102.1 [5290:1.1] Suffolk
SVFFOLCIÆ | Nova et Accurata | DELINEATIO
New and accurate map of Suffolk
Joannes Janßonius Excudit
38 x 49 cm.

Notes   Title flanked by a man and a woman in armour, beneath the title is the royal coat-of-arms.

Occurrence in atlases

1:432 Des Nieuwen Atlantis Aenhang, Janssonius, 1644: 10 k

1:434/36 Nieuwen Atlas... Het Vierde deel, Janssonius, 1647-49/1658: v4 19 2X

102.2 [5290:1.2] Suffolk
SUFFOLCIA | vernacula | SUFFOLKE
Suffolcia, in the vernacular Suffolk
Joannes Janßonius Excudit

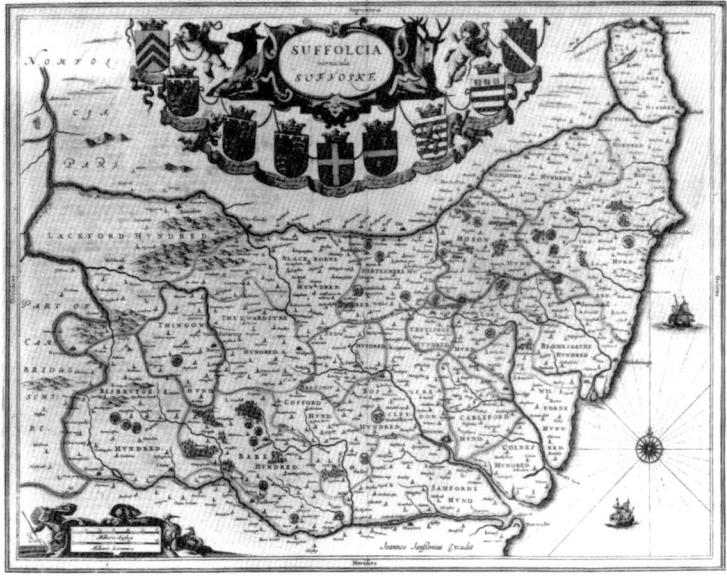

Notes Eight coats of arms of noble families are placed in a half-circle around the title cartouche.

Occurrence in atlases

1:403/05 Atlas Novus, Janssonius, 1647/1657-62: v4 19 3N 187-188
1:414/15 Le Nouvel Atlas... Tome Quatrieme, Janssonius, 1646-49: v4 19 3Y 211-212
1:425 Novus Atlas, Janssonius, 1647-49: v4 19 4E 245-246
1:434/36 Nieuwen Atlas... Het Vierde deel, Janssonius, 1647-49/1658: v4 19 2X
1:408 Atlas, Janssonius, after c. 1680: v3 18

103   [5290:2] Suffolk
SVFFOLCIA. | Vernacule | SVFFOLKE
Suffolcia, vernacularly Suffolk
38 x 49.5 cm.

Notes   The title cartouche is flanked by the coats of arms of East and West Suffolk; beside the cartouche are the coats of arms of the dukes and earls of Clarence and of Suffolk. The map has been copied from Speed's *Theatre*, edition after 1623, and was specially made for the atlas of England, which Joan Blaeu in 1645 joined as a fourth part to his *Atlas novus*.

Occurrence in atlases

2:301 Theatrum Orbis Terrarum sive Atlas Novus Pars Quarta, J. Blaeu, 1646: 21 4F 247-248

2:302-3 Theatrum Orbis Terrarum sive Atlas Novus Pars Quarta, J. Blaeu, 1646-48: 21 3X 212-213

2:311 Le Theatre du Monde ou Nouvel Atlas, Quatriesme Partie, J. Blaeu: 21 3V(3T) 215-216

2:312 Cinquème Volume de la Geographie Blaviane, J. Blaeu, 1663-67: 21 3O 181-182

2:321 Toonneel des Aerdycks oft Nieuwe Atlas... Vierde deel, J. Blaeu, 1648: 21 4C 233-234

2:322 Toonneel des Aerdycks oft Nieuwe Atlas... Vierde deel, J. Blaeu, 1648: 21 3R 201-202

2:331 Novus Atlas and Atlas Major (Vierter Teil), J. Blaeu, 1645-48: 21 4G 243-244

Nuevo Atlas del Reyno de Inglaterra, J. Blaeu, 1645/48: 21 4B 225-226

References   Van der Krogt 2002 18:34.

104   [5290:373] **Suffolk**
SVFFOLCIA.
Suffolk
8.5 x 12 cm.

Notes   This map is from a collection of 44 maps of the British Isles, engraved by Pieter van den Keere. The maps are comparable in size to those of the *Tabularum Geographicarum*, published by Pieter Bertius, for which Van den Keere engraved many maps. Although the maps of Van den Keere form one collection, no title-page is known.

Occurrence in atlases
373:01 Atlas of the British Isles, Van den Keere, c. 1605: 13
373:02 Britannia, Camden, 1617: 13 S5v 282

References   Skelton 1970, 4.

105.1 [5295:1.1] Norfolk
       NORFOLCIÆ | DESCRIPTIO. | The DESCRIPTION of | NOR-
       FOLK
       Map of Norfolk
       Amstelodami, | apud | Ioannem Ianßonium
       38 x 50 cm.

Notes   Situated on the east coast of England, Norfolk was vulnerable to in-
vasions from Scandinavia and northern Europe, and forts were built to defend
against the Angles and Saxons. By the fifth century the Angles, after whom East
Anglia and England itself are named, had established control of the region and
later became the 'north folk' and the 'south folk', hence Norfolk and Suffolk.

Occurrence in atlases
1:324 Appendix Atlantis, Janssonius, 1636: 15 O
1:323 Newer Atlas, Janssonius, 1636: VI 23 X(O)
1:332 Appendix Atlantis, Janssonius/Hondius, 1637: 13 R
1:421/2 Newer Atlas, Janssonius, 1638: VI 18 O
1:431 Nieuwen Atlas, Janssonius, 1638-44: VI 17 Y*

105.2   [5295:1.2] Norfolk
NORTFOLCIA; | vernacule | NORFOLKE
In the vernacular Norfolk
Amstelodami | apud | Ioannem Ianßonium
38 x 50 cm.

Notes   Norfolk, and several adjacent areas, became the kingdom of East Anglia, later merging with Mercia and then Wessex. The influence of the Early English settlers can be seen in the many instances of the elements 'thorpe', 'ton' and 'ham' in placenames.

Occurrence in atlases
1:403/05 Atlas Novus, Janssonius, 1647/1657-62: v4 20 3Q 195-196
1:414/15 Le Nouvel Atlas... Tome Quatrieme, Janssonius, 1646-49: v4 20 4A 217-218
1:425 Novus Atlas, Janssonius, 1647-49: v4 20 4H 253-254
1:434/36 Nieuwen Atlas... Het Vierde deel, Janssonius, 1647-49/1658: v4 20 2Y 131-132
1:408 Atlas, Janssonius, after c. 1680: v3 19

106   [5295:2] Norfolk
       NORTFOLCIA, | NORFOLKE
       Norfolk
       38 x 50 cm.

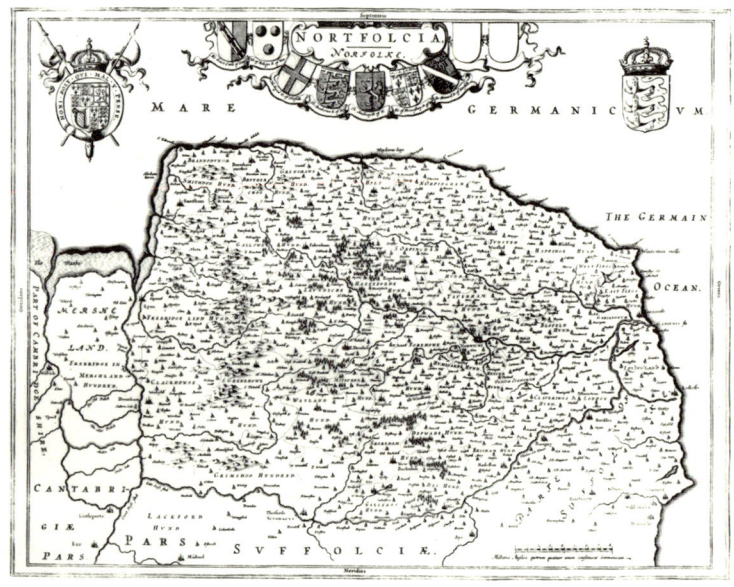

Notes   Around the title cartouche are the coats of arms of the earls and dukes of Norfolk. The map has been copied from Speed's *Theatre*, edition after 1623, and was specially made for the atlas of England, which Joan Blaeu in 1645 joined as a fourth part to his *Atlas novus*.

Occurrence in atlases

2:301 Theatrum Orbis Terrarum sive Atlas Novus Pars Quarta, J. Blaeu, 1646: 22 4I 257-258

2:302-3 Theatrum Orbis Terrarum sive Atlas Novus Pars Quarta, J. Blaeu, 1646-48: 22 4A 219-220

2:311 Le Theatre du Monde ou Nouvel Atlas, Quatriesme Partie, J. Blaeu: 22 3Y 221-222

2:312 Cinquème Volume de la Geographie Blaviane, J. Blaeu, 1663-67: 22 3Q 187-188

2:321 Toonneel des Aerdycks oft Nieuwe Atlas... Vierde deel, J. Blaeu, 1648: 22 4F 241-242

2:322 Toonneel des Aerdycks oft Nieuwe Atlas... Vierde deel, J. Blaeu, 1648: 22 3T 207-208

2:331 Novus Atlas and Atlas Major (Vierter Teil), J. Blaeu, 1645-48: 22 4K 251-252

Nuevo Atlas del Reyno de Inglaterra, J. Blaeu, 1645/48: 22 4E 233-234

References   Van der Krogt 2002 18:35.

107.1   [5295:352.1] Norfolk
NORFOLCIÆ | DESCRIPTIO
Map of Norfolk
Petrus Kærius Cælavit.
16 x 20.5 cm.

Notes   The only city in Norfolk is Norwich. During the eleventh century Norwich was the second largest city in England, after London, and one of the most important places in the kingdom.

Occurrence in atlases

352:32/33 Atlas Minor, Janssonius, 1648-51: VI 13 G2r 51

107.2 [5295:352.2] Norfolk
LE COMTÉ DE | NORFOLK.
The County of Norfolk

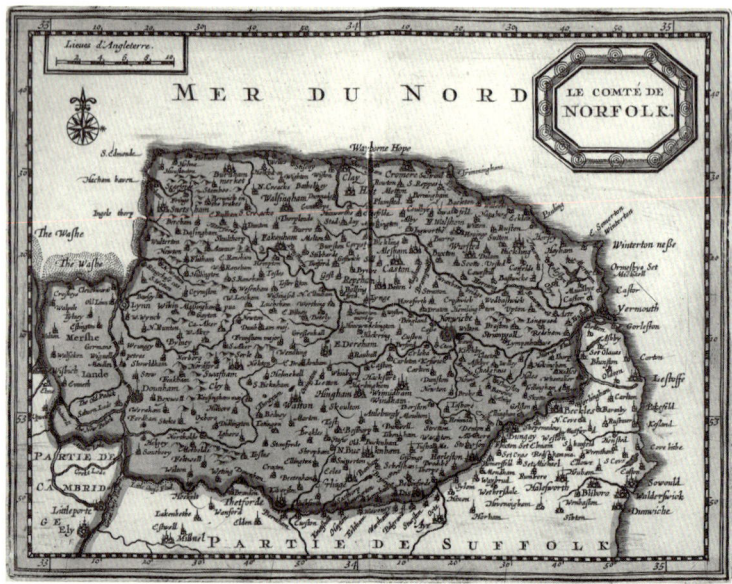

Notes   This map appeared in the *Atlas soulagé de son gros & pesant fardeau*, published by Pieter van der Aa. Almost all the maps are printed from reworked plates of Janssonius's *Atlas Minor*. The titles and scale were translated into French. Several Latin texts on the maps have been removed, as have the Latin names of the wind directions in the borders. The cartouches have been modernized and windroses added. Other modernizations are the removal of ships and sea monsters, and erasing names in curled letters and replacing them with Roman type letters. Latin names of seas and countries are often translated into French.

Occurrence in atlases
352:51.2-9 Atlas soulagé..., Van der Aa, c. 1714: v4 9 blank

108   [5295:373] Norfolk
NORFOLCIA
Norfolk
P. Kærius cælavit.
8.5 x 12.5 cm.

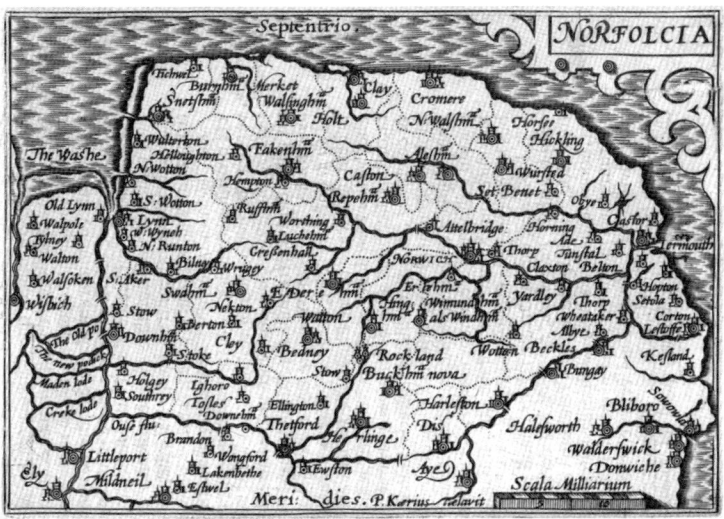

Notes   This map is from a collection of 44 maps of the British Isles, engraved by Pieter van den Keere. The maps are comparable in size to those of the *Tabularum Geographicarum*, published by Pieter Bertius, for which Van den Keere engraved many maps. Although the maps of Van den Keere form one collection, no title-page is known.

Occurrence in atlases
373:01 Atlas of the British Isles, Van den Keere, c. 1605: 14
373:02 Britannia, Camden, 1617: 14 T3r 293

References   Skelton 1970, 4.

109.1   [5300:1.1] Cambridgeshire
Comitatus | CANTABRI- | GIENSIS | Sive | CAMBRIDG | SHIRE
The county of Cambridge or Cambridgeshire
41.5 X 51.5 cm.

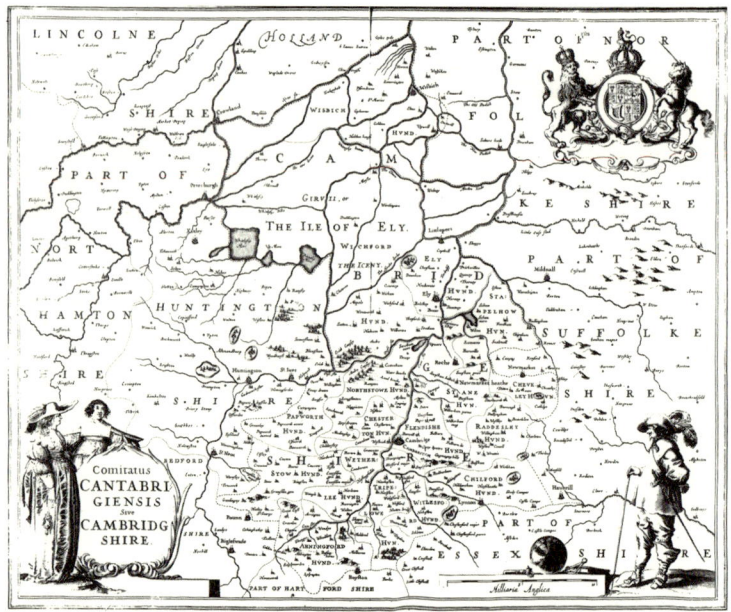

Notes   The title cartouche is decorated with costumed figures; at the top right
is the royal coat-of-arms. There are no other coats-of-arms.

Occurrence in atlases

1:432 Des Nieuwen Atlantis Aenhang, Janssonius, 1644: 4 d
1:434/36 Nieuwen Atlas... Het Vierde deel, Janssonius, 1647-49/1658: v4 21 2Z

109.2 [5300:1.2] Cambridgeshire
COMITATIS | CANTABRI- | GIENSIS; | vernacule | CAM-
BRIDGE | SHIRE
The county of Cambridge, vernacularly Cambridgeshire
Amstelodami | apud Joannem Janßonium.

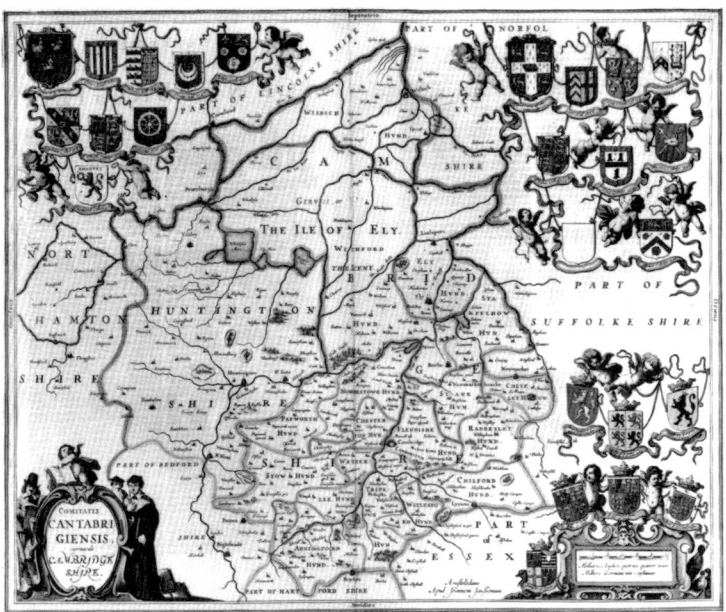

Notes A map of Cambridgeshire and Huntingdonshire with figurative cartouche, scale of miles and 25 coats of arms supported by numerous cherubs.

Occurrence in atlases

1:403/05 Atlas Novus, Janssonius, 1647/1657-62: v4 21 3S 201-202

1:414/15 Le Nouvel Atlas... Tome Quatrieme, Janssonius, 1646-49: v4 21 4C 223-
224

1:425 Novus Atlas, Janssonius, 1647-49: v4 21 4L 261-262

1:434/36 Nieuwen Atlas... Het Vierde deel, Janssonius, 1647-49/1658: v4 21 2Z

1:408 Atlas, Janssonius, after c. 1680: v3 20

110   [5300:2] Cambridgeshire
CANTABRIGIENSIS | COMITATVS; | CAMBRIDGE SHIRE
The county of Cambridge; Cambridgeshire
41.5 x 52 cm.

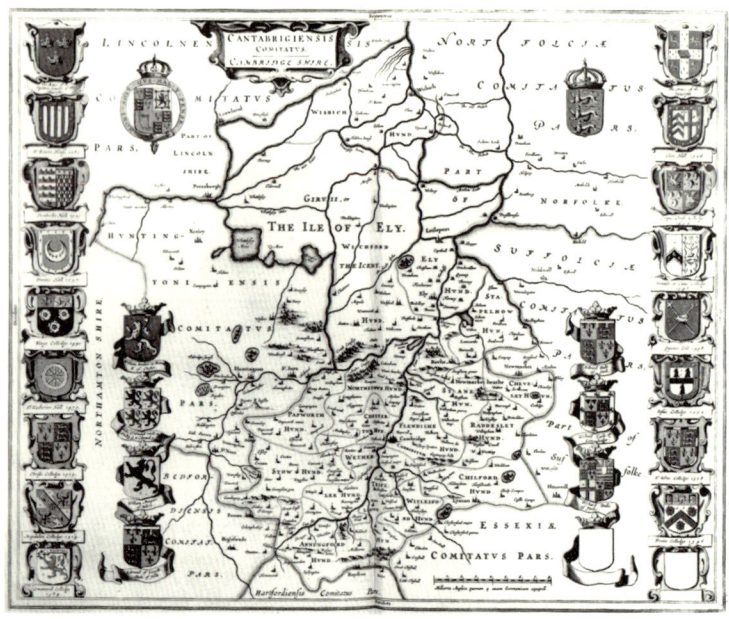

Notes   Around the map are 28 coats of arms (two of which are empty). At the edges left and right are the coats of arms of the founders and the colleges of the University of Cambridge. At the top left and right are the royal coat of arms and the coat of arms of England, and at the bottom the coats of arms of some dukes of York and earls of Cambridge. The map has been copied from Speed's *Theatre*, edition after 1623, and was specially made for the atlas of England, which Joan Blaeu in 1645 joined as a fourth part to his *Atlas novus*.

Occurrence in atlases

2:301 Theatrum Orbis Terrarum sive Atlas Novus Pars Quarta, J. Blaeu, 1646: 24 4L 263-264

2:302-3 Theatrum Orbis Terrarum sive Atlas Novus Pars Quarta, J. Blaeu, 1646-48: 24 4D 227-228

2:311 Le Theatre du Monde ou Nouvel Atlas, Quatriesme Partie, J. Blaeu: 24 4A 227-228

2:312 Cinquème Volume de la Geographie Blaviane, J. Blaeu, 1663-67: 24 3T 193-194

2:321 Toonneel des Aerdycks oft Nieuwe Atlas... Vierde deel, J. Blaeu, 1648: 24 4I 249-250

2:322 Toonneel des Aerdycks oft Nieuwe Atlas... Vierde deel, J. Blaeu, 1648: 24 3Y 213-214

2:331 Novus Atlas and Atlas Major (Vierter Teil), J. Blaeu, 1645-48: 24 4N
259-260
Nuevo Atlas del Reyno de Inglaterra, J. Blaeu, 1645/48: 24 4H 241-242

References Van der Krogt 2002 18:37.

III.I [5300:352.1] Cambridgeshire
CANTABRI- | GIENSIS | COMITATVS | DESCRIPTIO.
Map of the county of Cambridge
15 x 20 cm.

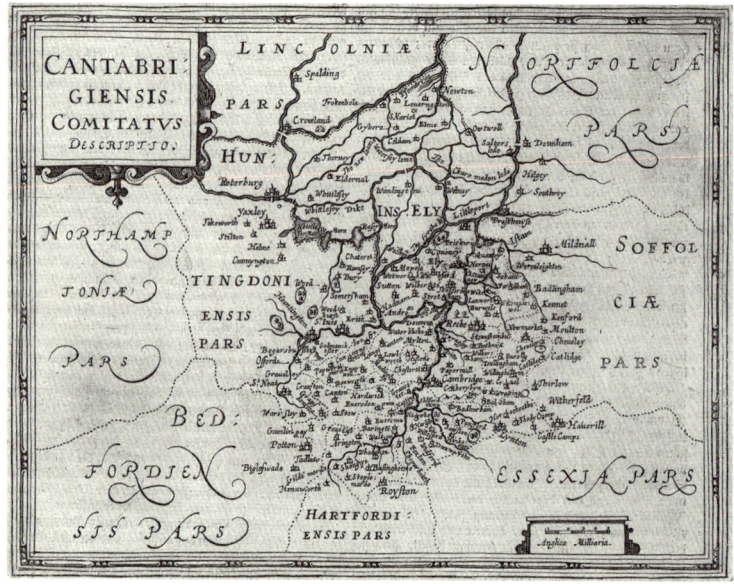

Notes Cambridgeshire is recorded in the Domesday Book (1086) as 'Grant-bridgeshire' (*Grentebrigescire*) (after the river Granta, another name for the river Cam). Covering a large part of East Anglia, Cambridgeshire today is the result of several local government unifications.

Occurrence in atlases

352:32/33 Atlas Minor, Janssonius, 1648-51: VI 15 H2r 59

111.2   [5300:352.2] Cambridgeshire
COMTÉ | DE | CAMBRIDGE.
The county of Cambridge

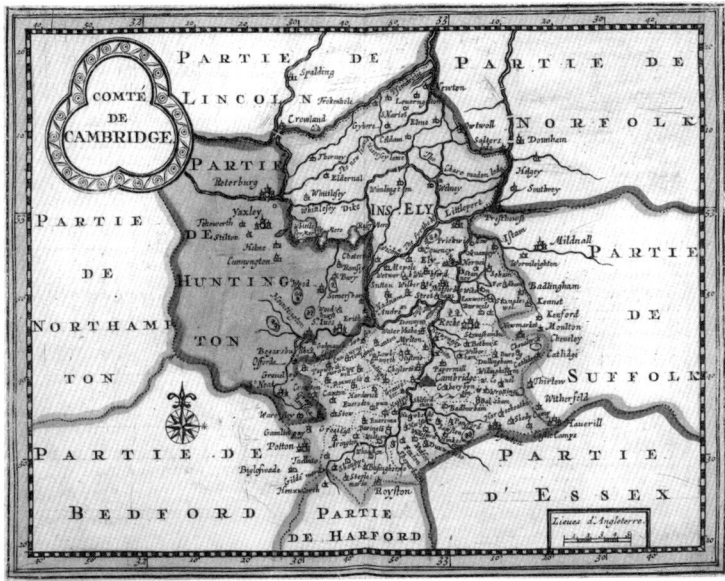

Notes   This map appeared in the *Atlas soulagé de son gros & pesant fardeau*, published by Pieter van der Aa. Almost all the maps are printed from reworked plates
of Janssonius's *Atlas Minor*. The titles and scale were translated into French. Several Latin texts on the maps have been removed, as have the Latin names of the
wind directions in the borders. The cartouches have been modernized and windroses added. Other modernizations are the removal of ships and sea monsters,
and erasing names in curled letters and replacing them with Roman type letters.
Latin names of seas and countries are often translated into French.

Occurrence in atlases
352:51.2-9 Atlas soulagé..., Van der Aa, c. 1714: v4 10 blank

112   **[5305:1] Huntingdonshire**
HVNTINGDONENSIS | COMITATVS | HUNTINGTON |
SHIRE
The county of Huntingdon. Huntingdonshire
39.5 X 50 cm.

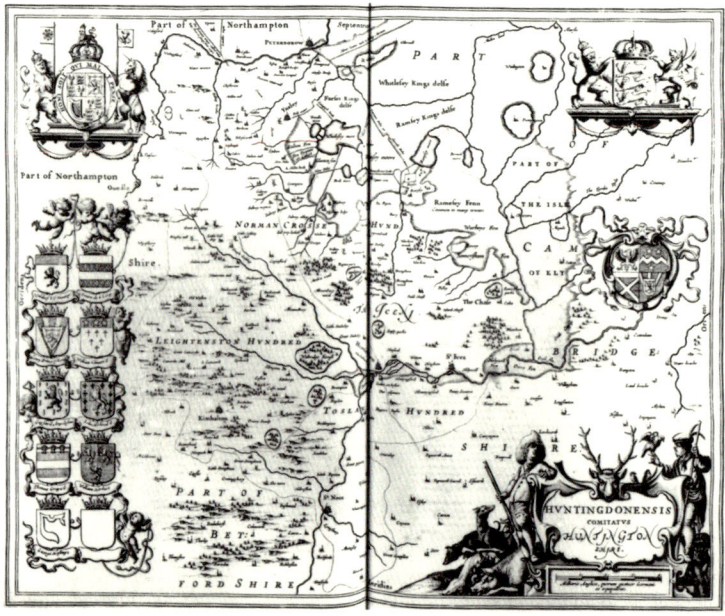

Notes   Above left is the royal coat of arms. The motto in the coat is: Honi soit qui mal y pense, which means 'Shame be to him who thinks evil of it', the motto of the Order of the Garter. Above right is the coat of arms of England. On the left of the map there are also some coats of arms of noble families.

Occurrence in atlases

1:403/05 Atlas Novus, Janssonius, 1647/1657-62: v4 22 3V 205-206

1:414/15 Le Nouvel Atlas... Tome Quatrieme, Janssonius, 1646-49: v4 22 4E 229-230

1:425 Novus Atlas, Janssonius, 1647-49: v4 22 4N 267-268

1:434/36 Nieuwen Atlas... Het Vierde deel, Janssonius, 1647-49/1658: v4 22 2Z2

1:408 Atlas, Janssonius, after c. 1680: v3 21

113   [5305:2] Huntingdonshire
HVNTINGDO- | NENSIS COMITATVS; | HUNTINGTON
SHIRE
The county of Huntingdon; Huntingdonshire
39 X 50 cm.

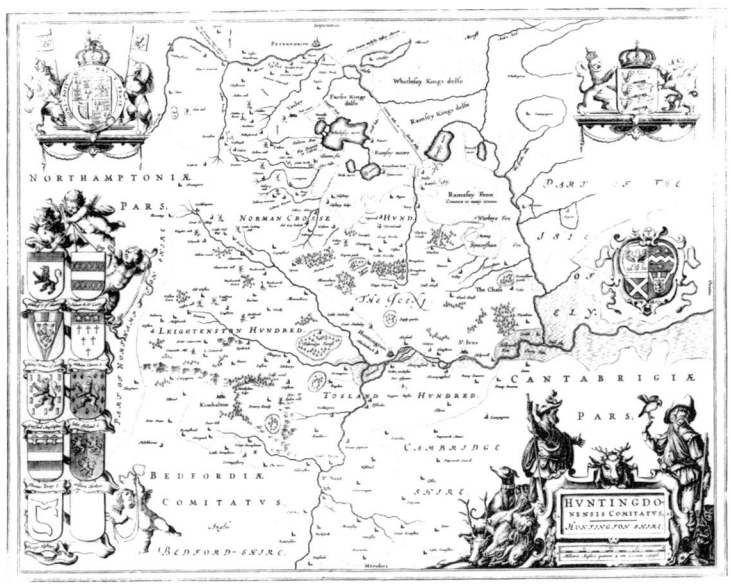

Notes   The title cartouche is surrounded by images of hunters and their booty, possibly a reference to the name of the county. To the right of the map is the coat of arms of the county and to the left that of the earls of Huntingdon. The map has been copied from Speed's *Theatre*, edition after 1623, and was specially made for the atlas of England, which Joan Blaeu in 1645 joined as a fourth part to his *Atlas novus*.

Occurrence in atlases   2:301 Theatrum Orbis Terrarum sive Atlas Novus Pars
    Quarta, J. Blaeu, 1646: 25 4O 271-272
2:302-3 Theatrum Orbis Terrarum sive Atlas Novus Pars Quarta, J. Blaeu, 1646-48: 25 4F 233-234
2:311 Le Theatre du Monde ou Nouvel Atlas, Quatriesme Partie, J. Blaeu: 25 4C 233-234
2:312 Cinquème Volume de la Geographie Blaviane, J. Blaeu, 1663-67: 25 3X 197-198
2:321 Toonneel des Aerdycks oft Nieuwe Atlas... Vierde deel, J. Blaeu, 1648: 25 4L 255-256
2:322 Toonneel des Aerdycks oft Nieuwe Atlas... Vierde deel, J. Blaeu, 1648: 25 4A 219-220
2:331 Novus Atlas and Atlas Major (Vierter Teil), J. Blaeu, 1645-48: 25 4P 265
Nuevo Atlas del Reyno de Inglaterra, J. Blaeu, 1645/48: 25 4K 247-248

References   Van der Krogt 2002 18:38.

114.1   [5310:1.1] The Fenns
        A general Plott | and description of | the Fennes and sur | ounded
        grounds in | the sixe Counties of | Norfolke, Suffolke, | Cambridge, with
        in | the Isle of Ely, Hun- | tington, Northamp- | ton and Lincolne | etc
        AMSTELODAMI, | Sumptibus Henrici Hondii. 1632
        44 x 55.5 cm.

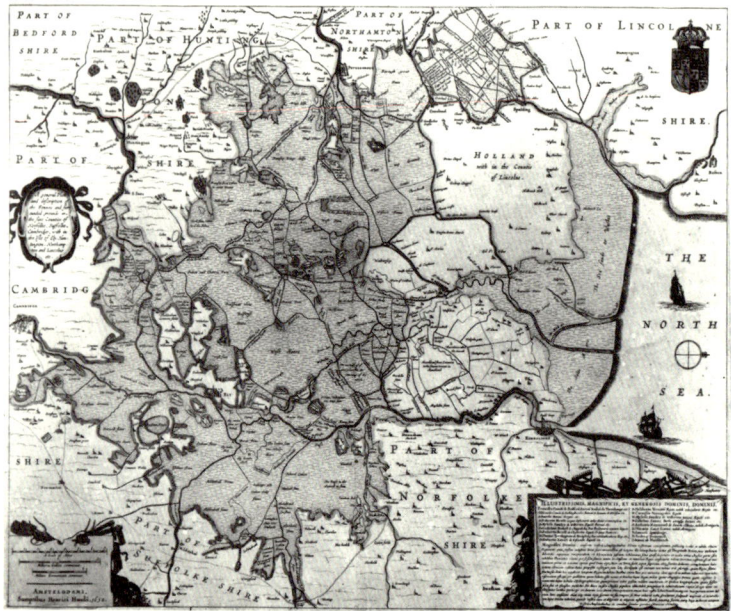

Notes   The map is dedicated by Hondius to 18 noble men, of who Francis Russell
(1593-1641), the 4th Earl of Bedfordshire, the most important one was.

Flooded areas on the map has been extra emphasised by the colouring, to which
result a dramatic impact has arisen. The origin of the name ' Isle or Ely' (Island
of Ely) for the area around the city Ely (left of the middle on the map) is clearly
illustrated. Between 1630 and 1637 the Dutch hydraulic engineer Cornelius Vermuyden worked there for a system of water ways and reclamations to bring the
area in culture. Original this map has undoubtedly a relation with these activities.

Occurrence in atlases

1:311 Atlas, Hondius, 1633: VI 25 2M2 137-140

1:312 L´Appendice de L´Atlas, Hondius, 1633: 4 2M2 137-140

1:341 Hondius-Janssonius, 1636-41: VI 12 Z 65-66

1:301 Appendix Novi Atlantis, Janssonius, 1637: 5 d

1:401 Atlas Novus, Janssonius-Hondius, 1638: VI 25 2C

1:411/2 Nouveau Theatre du Monde, Hondius, 1639-42: VI 25 2A

114.2 [5310:1.2] The Fenns
A general Plott | and description of | the Fennes and sur | ounded
grounds in | the six Counties of | Norfolke, Suffolke, | Cambridge,
with in | the Isle of Ely, Hun- | tington, Northamp- | ton and
Lincolne | etc
Amstelodami, Sumptibus Ioannis Ianssonii

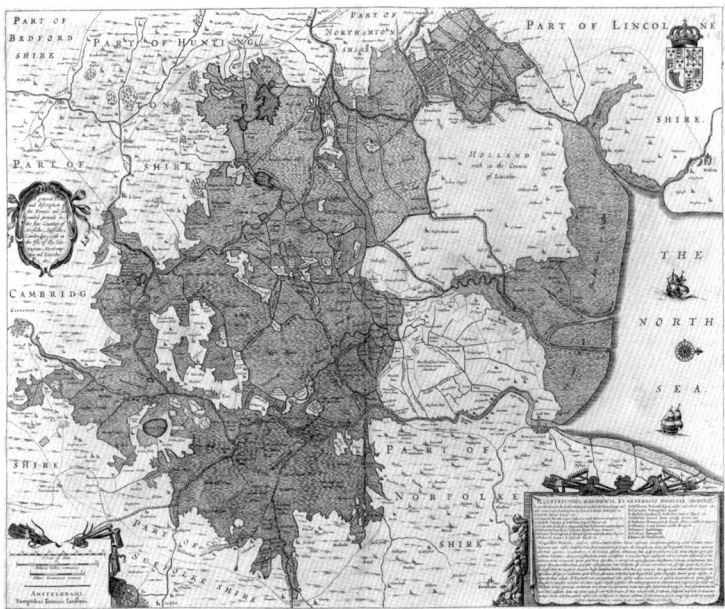

Notes   The map is dedicated by Hondius to 18 noble men, of whom Francis Russell (1593–1641), the fourth Earl of Bedford, was the most important.

Occurrence in atlases
1:403/05 Atlas Novus, Janssonius, 1647/1657-62: v4 23 3Y 209-210
1:414/15 Le Nouvel Atlas... Tome Quatrieme, Janssonius, 1646-49: v4 23 4F 231-
232
1:425 Novus Atlas, Janssonius, 1647-49: v4 23 4P 271-272
1:434/36 Nieuwen Atlas... Het Vierde deel, Janssonius, 1647-49/1658: v4 23 2Z3
1:408 Atlas, Janssonius, after c. 1680: v3 22

115   [5310:2] The Fenns
REGIONES | INVNDATÆ | In finibus Comitatus | NORFOLCIÆ,
SVFFOLCIÆ, | CANTABRIGÆ, HVNTINGTONIÆ | NORTH-
AMTONIÆ, et | LINCOLNIÆ
The flooded areas within the borders of the counties Norfolk, Suffolk,
Cambridgeshire, Huntingdonshire, Northamptonshire and Lincolnshire
43.5 x 54 cm.

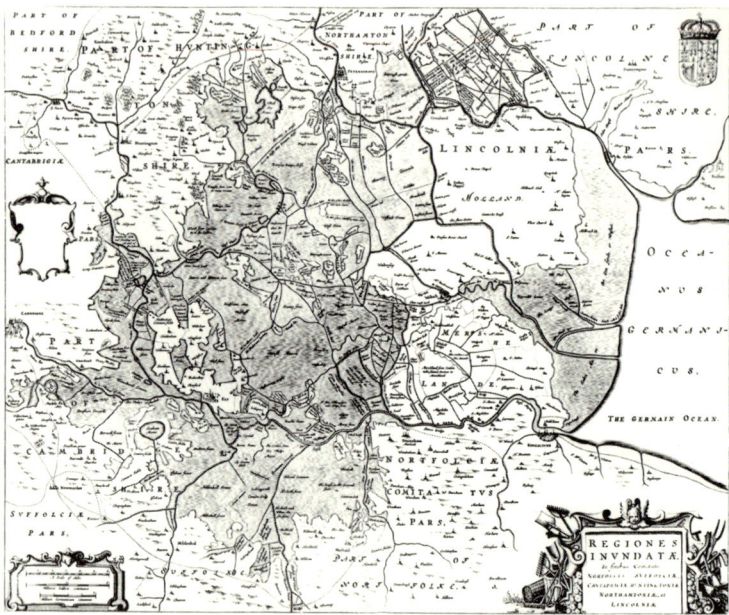

Notes   The flooded areas on the map have been emphasized by colouring, with
dramatic effect. The origin of the name 'Isle of Ely' for the area around the city Ely
(left of the middle on the map) is clearly illustrated. Between 1630 and 1637 the
Dutch hydraulic engineer Cornelius Vermuyden was engaged to create a system of
waterways and land reclamation to bring the area into cultivation. The origin of this
map is undoubtedly related to these activities. The map has been copied from the
map of Henricus Hondius from 1632, 'A general plott and description of the Fennes'
(joined as from 1633 in the Mercator-Hondius atlases (5310:1.1 and 2, above)).

Occurrence in atlases
2:301 Theatrum Orbis Terrarum sive Atlas Novus Pars Quarta, J. Blaeu, 1646: 23
blank
2:302-3 Theatrum Orbis Terrarum sive Atlas Novus Pars Quarta, J. Blaeu, 1646-
48: 23 4B 221-222
2:311 Le Theatre du Monde ou Nouvel Atlas, Quatriesme Partie, J. Blaeu: 23 blank
2:312 Cinquème Volume de la Geographie Blaviane, J. Blaeu, 1663-67: 23 3R 189-
190

2:321 Toonneel des Aerdycks oft Nieuwe Atlas... Vierde deel, J. Blaeu, 1648: 23
4G 243-244
2:322 Toonneel des Aerdycks oft Nieuwe Atlas... Vierde deel, J. Blaeu, 1648: 23
3V 209-210
2:331 Novus Atlas and Atlas Major (Vierter Teil), J. Blaeu, 1645-48: 23 blank
Nuevo Atlas del Reyno de Inglaterra, J. Blaeu, 1645/48: 23 4F 235-236

References Van der Krogt 2002 18:36.

116   [5315:1] Northamptonshire
COMITATVS | NORTHANTONENSIS | vernacule | NORTH-
AMPTON SHIRE
The county of Northampton, vernacularly Northamptonshire
39 X 51 cm.

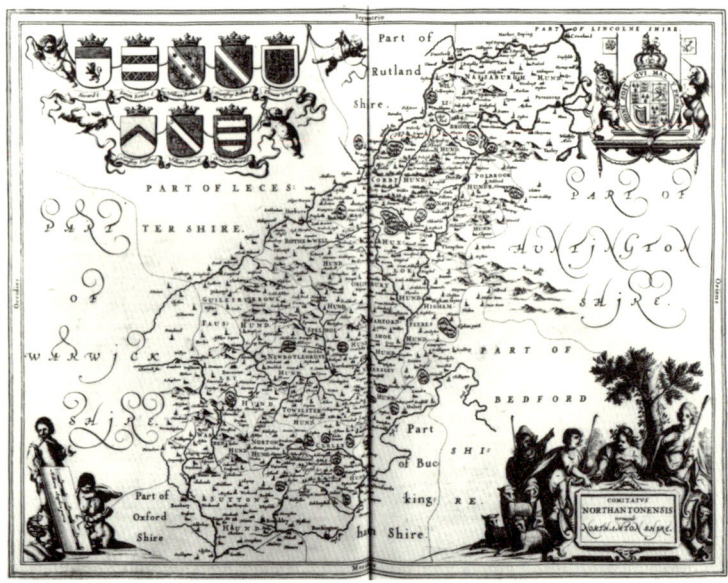

Notes   At the top right is the royal coat of arms. The motto is: 'Honi soit qui mal
y pense', which means 'Shame be to him who thinks evil of it', and is the motto of
the Order of the Garter. Above right is the coat of arms of England. Left of the
map there are also some coats of arms of noble families.

Occurrence in atlases
1:403/05 Atlas Novus, Janssonius, 1647/1657-62: v4 24 3Z 211-212
1:414/15 Le Nouvel Atlas... Tome Quatrieme, Janssonius, 1646-49: v4 24 4G 233-
234
1:425 Novus Atlas, Janssonius, 1647-49: v4 24 4Q 273-274
1:434/36 Nieuwen Atlas... Het Vierde deel, Janssonius, 1647-49/1658: v4 24 2Z4
1:408 Atlas, Janssonius, after c. 1680: v3 26

117   [5315:2] Northamptonshire
COMITATVS | NORTHANTO- | NENSIS; | Vernacule | NORTH-
AMTON SHIRE
The county of Northampton, vernacularly Northamptonshire
41 X 49 cm.

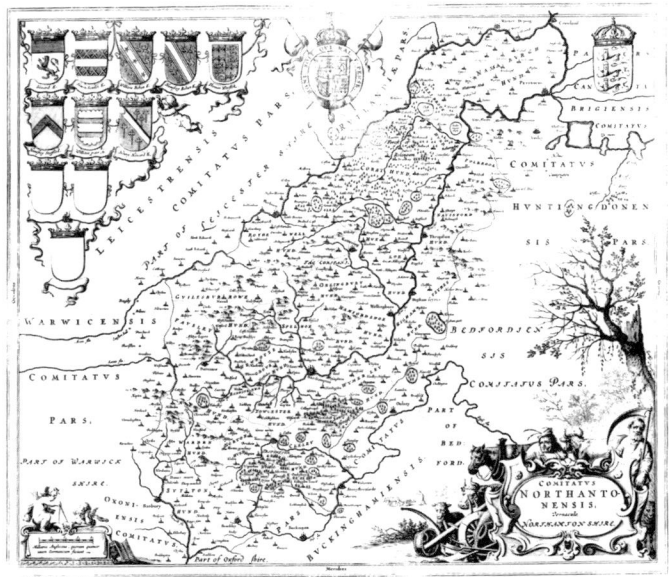

Notes   The title cartouche is decorated with images of farmers and their cattle
and tools. The county still has a predominantly agricultural economy. Above are
the coats of arms of the earls of Northampton. The map has been copied from
Speed's *Theatre*, edition after 1623, and was specially made for the atlas of England,
which Joan Blaeu in 1645 joined as a fourth part to his *Atlas novus*.

Occurrence in atlases   2:301 Theatrum Orbis Terrarum sive Atlas Novus Pars
    Quarta, J. Blaeu, 1646: 26 4Q 275-276
2:302-3 Theatrum Orbis Terrarum sive Atlas Novus Pars Quarta, J. Blaeu, 1646-
48: 26 4H 237-238
2:311 Le Theatre du Monde ou Nouvel Atlas, Quatriesme Partie, J. Blaeu: 26 4D
235-236
2:312 Cinquème Volume de la Geographie Blaviane, J. Blaeu, 1663-67: 26 3Y 199-200
2:321 Toonneel des Aerdycks oft Nieuwe Atlas... Vierde deel, J. Blaeu, 1648: 26
4M 257-258
2:322 Toonneel des Aerdycks oft Nieuwe Atlas... Vierde deel, J. Blaeu, 1648: 26
4B 221-222
2:331 Novus Atlas and Atlas Major (Vierter Teil), J. Blaeu, 1645-48: 26 4R 269-270
Nuevo Atlas del Reyno de Inglaterra, J. Blaeu, 1645/48: 26 4M 251-252

References   Van der Krogt 2002 18:39.

118   [5315:373] Northamptonshire, Bedfordshire, Cambridge etc.
Northamtoniæ | Bedfordiæ Canta | brigæ Huntingdoniæ | et
Rutlandiæ Com.
The counties of Northampton, Bedford, Cambridge, Huntingdon
and Rutland
8.5 x 12 cm.

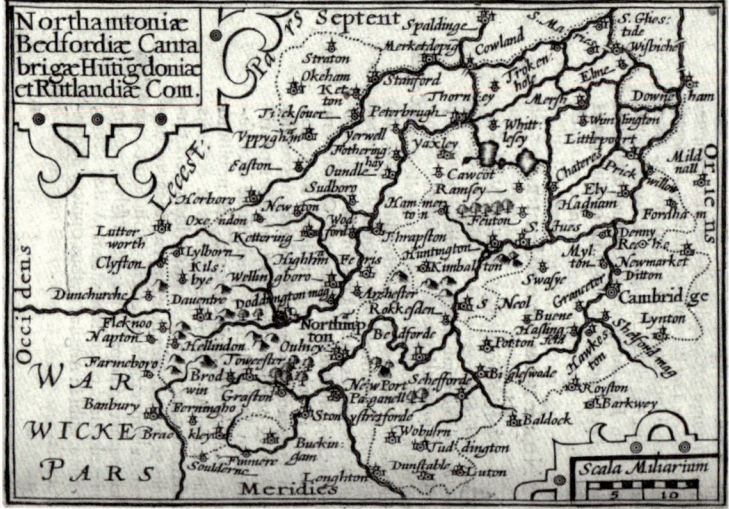

Notes   This map is from a collection of 44 maps of the British Isles, engraved by
Pieter van den Keere. The maps are comparable in size to those of the *Tabularum
Geographicarum*, published by Pieter Bertius, for which Van den Keere engraved
many maps. Although the maps of Van den Keere form one collection, no title-
page is known.

Occurrence in atlases
373:01 Atlas of the British Isles, Van den Keere, c. 1605: 15
373:02 Britannia, Camden, 1617: 15 V8v 320

References   Skelton 1970, 4.

119   [5320:1] Leicestershire
**LEICESTRENSIS | COMITATVS | cum RVTLANDIÆ. | Vulgo
Leicester & Rutland | Shire**
The county Leicester with Rutland. In the vulgar tongue Leicester and
Rutland shire
Amstelodami | Ex. Joannes Janßonius
44 x 55 cm.

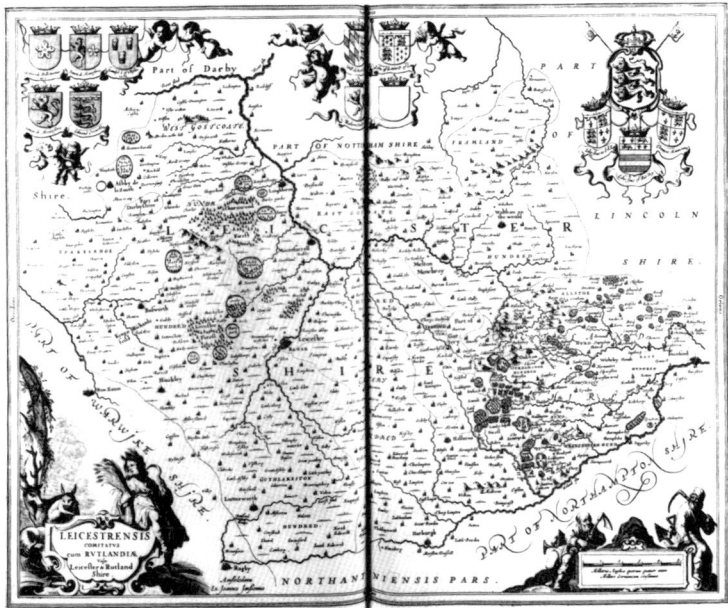

Notes   At the top left and the top middle there are nine coats of arms of noble
families, of which one is empty. At the top right is the coat of arms of England. The
scale cartouche is surrounded by some images of old men with farming equipment.

Occurrence in atlases
1:403/05 Atlas Novus, Janssonius, 1647/1657-62: v4 25 4B 217-218
1:414/15 Le Nouvel Atlas... Tome Quatrieme, Janssonius, 1646-49: v4 25 4I 237-
238
1:425 Novus Atlas, Janssonius, 1647-49: v4 25 4S 279-280
1:434/36 Nieuwen Atlas... Het Vierde deel, Janssonius, 1647-49/1658: v4 25 3A
135-136
1:408 Atlas, Janssonius, after c. 1680: v3 25

120   [5320:2] Leicestershire
LEICESTRENSIS | COMITATVS. | LEICESTER SHIRE
The county of Leicester. Leicestershire
38 x 49.5 cm.

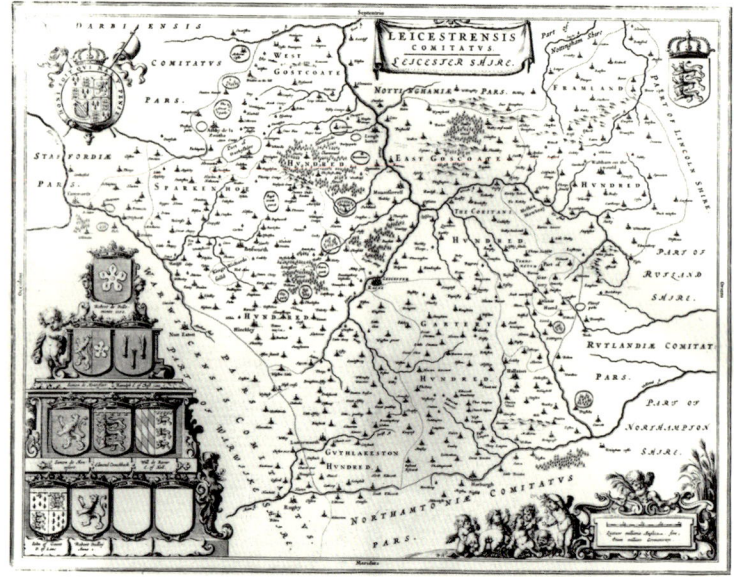

Notes   Left below are the coats of arms of the earls of Leicester. The map has been copied from Speed's *Theatre*, edition after 1623, and was specially made for the atlas of England, which Joan Blaeu in 1645 joined as a fourth part to his *Atlas novus*.

Occurrence in atlases

2:301 Theatrum Orbis Terrarum sive Atlas Novus Pars Quarta, J. Blaeu, 1646: 27 4S 281-282

2:302-3 Theatrum Orbis Terrarum sive Atlas Novus Pars Quarta, J. Blaeu, 1646-48: 27 4K 243-244

2:311 Le Theatre du Monde ou Nouvel Atlas, Quatriesme Partie, J. Blaeu: 27 4F 241-242

2:312 Cinquème Volume de la Geographie Blaviane, J. Blaeu, 1663-67: 27 4A 205-206

2:321 Toonneel des Aerdrycks oft Nieuwe Atlas... Vierde deel, J. Blaeu, 1648: 27 4P 265-266

2:322 Toonneel des Aerdrycks oft Nieuwe Atlas... Vierde deel, J. Blaeu, 1648: 27 4D 227-228

2:331 Novus Atlas and Atlas Major (Vierter Teil), J. Blaeu, 1645-48: 27 4T 275-276

Nuevo Atlas del Reyno de Inglaterra, J. Blaeu, 1645/48: 27 4P 259-260

References   Van der Krogt 2002 18:40.

121   [5320:373] Leicestershire and Warwickshire
Warwic & | Lecestria | 1599
Warwickshire and Leicestershire 1599
Pe. | Kærius | cælavit.
8.5 x 12 cm.

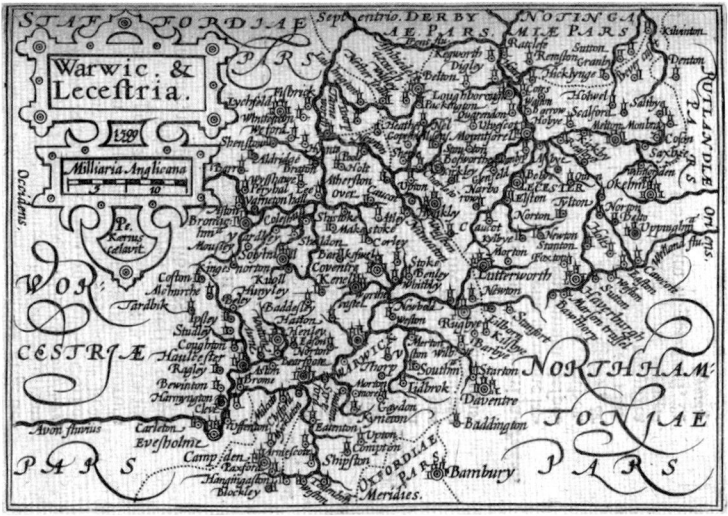

Notes   This map is from a collection of 44 maps of the British Isles, engraved by
Pieter van den Keere. The maps are comparable in size to those of the *Tabularum
Geographicarum*, published by Pieter Bertius, for which Van den Keere engraved
many maps. Although the maps of Van den Keere form one collection, no title-
page is known.

Occurrence in atlases
373:01 Atlas of the British Isles, Van den Keere, c. 1605: 10
373:02 Britannia, Camden, 1617: 18 Z7v 366

References   Skelton 1970, 4.

122 [5325:2] Rutland
RVTLANDIA | COMITATVS. | RVTLAND SHIRE
The county of Rutland. Rutland shire
38 x 49.5 cm.

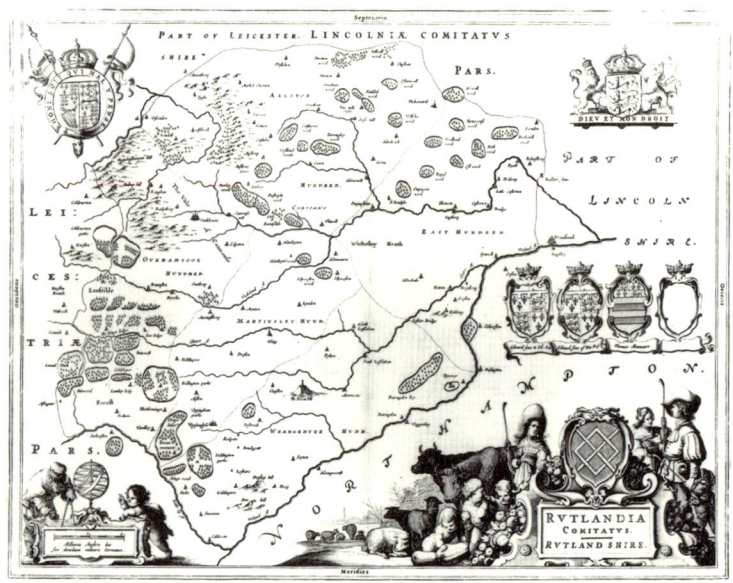

Notes On the right are the coats of arms of the earls of Rutland and near the title the coat of arms of the county itself. The map has been copied from Speed's *Theatre*, edition after 1623, and was specially made for the atlas of England, which Joan Blaeu in 1645 joined as a fourth part to his *Atlas novus*.

Occurrence in atlases

2:301 Theatrum Orbis Terrarum sive Atlas Novus Pars Quarta, J. Blaeu, 1646: 28 4V 285-286

2:302-3 Theatrum Orbis Terrarum sive Atlas Novus Pars Quarta, J. Blaeu, 1646-48: 28 4M 247-248

2:311 Le Theatre du Monde ou Nouvel Atlas, Quatriesme Partie, J. Blaeu: 28 4G 243-244

2:312 Cinquème Volume de la Geographie Blaviane, J. Blaeu, 1663-67: 28 4B 207-208

2:321 Toonneel des Aerdycks oft Nieuwe Atlas... Vierde deel, J. Blaeu, 1648: 28 4R 269-270

2:322 Toonneel des Aerdycks oft Nieuwe Atlas... Vierde deel, J. Blaeu, 1648: 28 4E 229-230

2:331 Novus Atlas and Atlas Major (Vierter Teil), J. Blaeu, 1645-48: 28 4X 279-280

Nuevo Atlas del Reyno de Inglaterra, J. Blaeu, 1645/48: 28 4R 263-264

References Van der Krogt 2002 18:41.

123   [5330:1] Lincolnshire
LINCOLNIA | COMITATVS | Anglis | LYNCOLNE SHIRE
The county of Lincoln, in English Lincolnshire
40 x 50 cm.

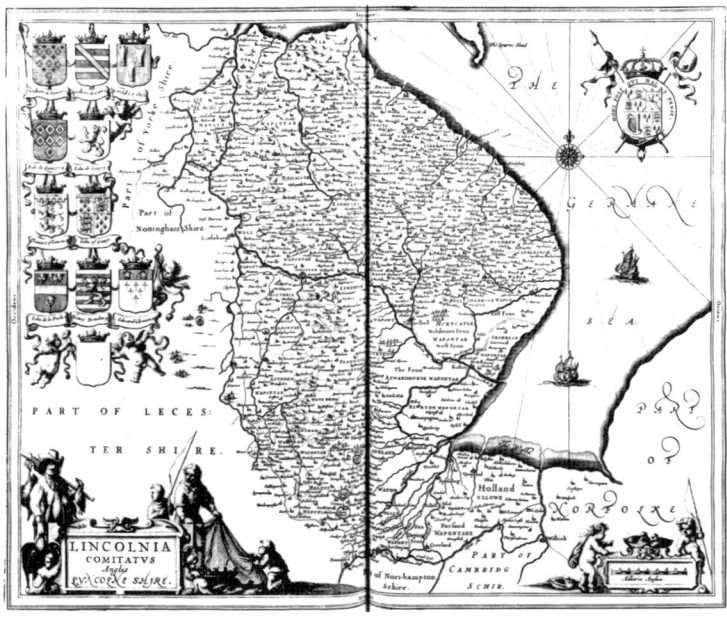

Notes   Left on the map are the coats of arms of nine noble families, of which one is empty. Above right is the royal coat of arms. The motto in the coat is: Honi soit qui mal y pense, which means 'Shame be to him who thinks evil of it', the motto of the Order of the Garter. The title cartouche is surrounded by images of a hunter and a fisherman.

Occurrence in atlases
1:403/05 Atlas Novus, Janssonius, 1647/1657-62: v4 26 4D 223-224
1:414/15 Le Nouvel Atlas... Tome Quatrieme, Janssonius, 1646-49: v4 26 4L 243-244
1:425 Novus Atlas, Janssonius, 1647-49: v4 26 4V 285-286
1:434/36 Nieuwen Atlas... Het Vierde deel, Janssonius, 1647-49/1658: v4 26 3B2
1:408 Atlas, Janssonius, after c. 1680: v3 24

124   [5330:2] Lincolnshire
LINCOLNIA | COMITATVS. Anglis | LINCOLN-SHIRE
The county of Lincoln. In English Lincolnshire
41.5 X 50 cm.

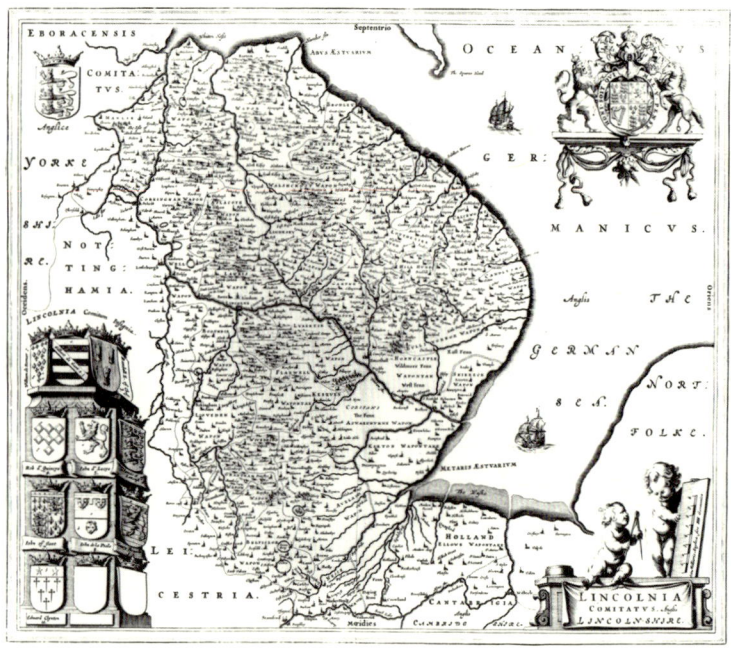

Notes   Left below are the coats of arms of the earls of Lincoln. The map has been copied from Speed's *Theatre*, edition after 1623, and was specially made for the atlas of England, which Joan Blaeu in 1645 joined as a fourth part to his *Atlas novus*.

Occurrence in atlases

2:301 Theatrum Orbis Terrarum sive Atlas Novus Pars Quarta, J. Blaeu, 1646: 29 4X 287-288

2:302-3 Theatrum Orbis Terrarum sive Atlas Novus Pars Quarta, J. Blaeu, 1646-48: 29 4N 249-250

2:311 Le Theatre du Monde ou Nouvel Atlas, Quatriesme Partie, J. Blaeu: 29 4H 245-246

2:312 Cinquème Volume de la Geographie Blaviane, J. Blaeu, 1663-67: 29 4C 209-210

2:321 Toonneel des Aerdycks oft Nieuwe Atlas... Vierde deel, J. Blaeu, 1648: 29 4S 271-272

2:322 Toonneel des Aerdycks oft Nieuwe Atlas... Vierde deel, J. Blaeu, 1648: 29 4F 231-232

2:331 Novus Atlas and Atlas Major (Vierter Teil), J. Blaeu, 1645-48: 29 4Y 281-282

Nuevo Atlas del Reyno de Inglaterra, J. Blaeu, 1645/48: 29 4S 265-266

References   Van der Krogt 2002 18:42.

125   [5330:373] Lincolnshire and Nottinghamshire
Lincolnia et | Notingham.
Lincolnshire and Nottinghamshire
8.5 x 12 cm.

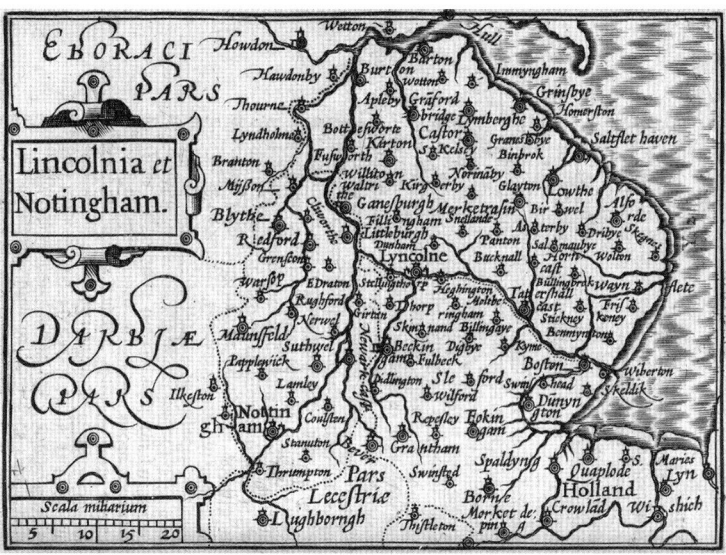

Notes   This map is from a collection of 44 maps from the British Isles, engraved by Pieter van den Keere. The maps have a comparable size of those of the *Tabularum Geographicarum*, published by Pieter Bertius, for which Van den Keere engraved many maps. Although the maps of Van den Keere form one collection, no title-page is known.

Occurrence in atlases

373:01 Atlas of the British Isles, Van den Keere, c. 1605: 16
373:02 Britannia, Camden, 1617: 16 Y2r 339

References   Skelton 1970, 4.

126.1   [5335:1.1] Nottinghamshire
COMITATVS | NOTTINGHA | MIENSIS | sive | The COVNTIE
of | NOTTIN- | GAM
The county of Nottingham
37.5 x 48 cm.

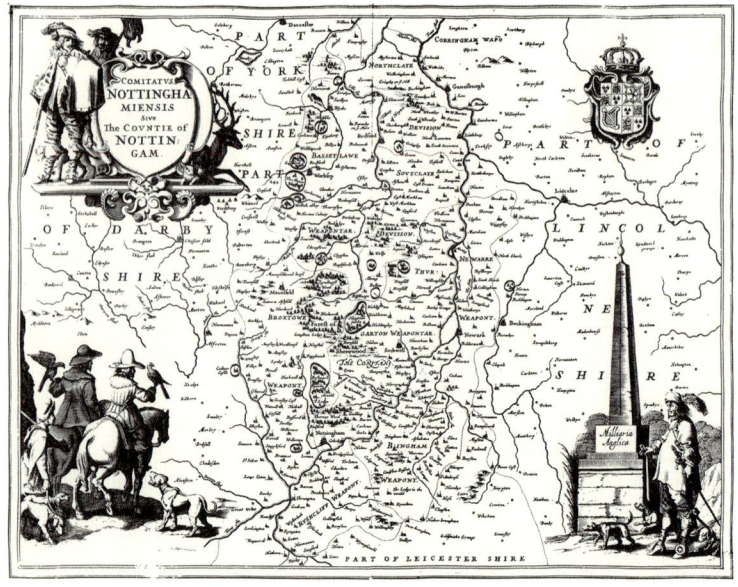

Notes   In this first state of this map the scale cartouche is an obelisk. Above this
obelisk is the royal coat of arms. Left below there are some noble men hunting.

Occurrence in atlases
1:432 Des Nieuwen Atlantis Aenhang, Janssonius, 1644: 2 b
1:434/36 Nieuwen Atlas... Het Vierde deel, Janssonius, 1647-49/1658: v4 27 3C

126.2 [5335:1.2] Nottinghamshire
**COMITATVS | NOTTINGHA- | MIENSIS; | Sive | NOTTING-
HAM | SHIRE**
The county Nottingham or Nottinghamshire

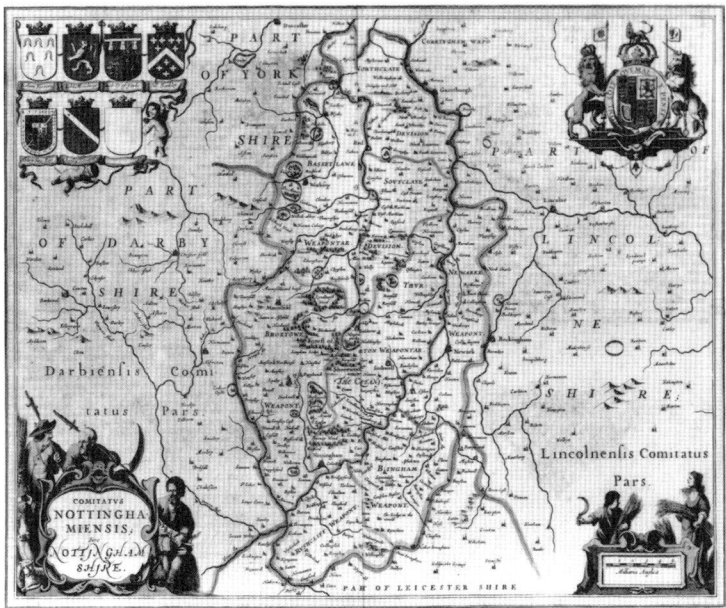

Notes   In this second state of this map, the obelisk is removed. The royal coat
of arms now contains the motto of the Order of the Garter: Honi soit qui mal y
pense, which means 'Shame be to him who thinks evil of it'. The hunting scene is
removed and some coats of arms of noble families are added.

Occurrence in atlases
1:403/05 Atlas Novus, Janssonius, 1647/1657-62: v4 27 4G 231-232
1:414/15 Le Nouvel Atlas... Tome Quatrieme, Janssonius, 1646-49: v4 27 4N 249-
250
1:425 Novus Atlas, Janssonius, 1647-49: v4 27 4Z 295-296
1:434/36 Nieuwen Atlas... Het Vierde deel, Janssonius, 1647-49/1658: v4 27 3C
1:408 Atlas, Janssonius, after c. 1680: v3 23

127 [5335:2] Nottinghamshire
COMITATVS | NOTTINGHA- | MIENSIS; | NOTTINGHAM SHIRE

The county Nottingham; Nottinghamshire

38.5 x 50 cm.

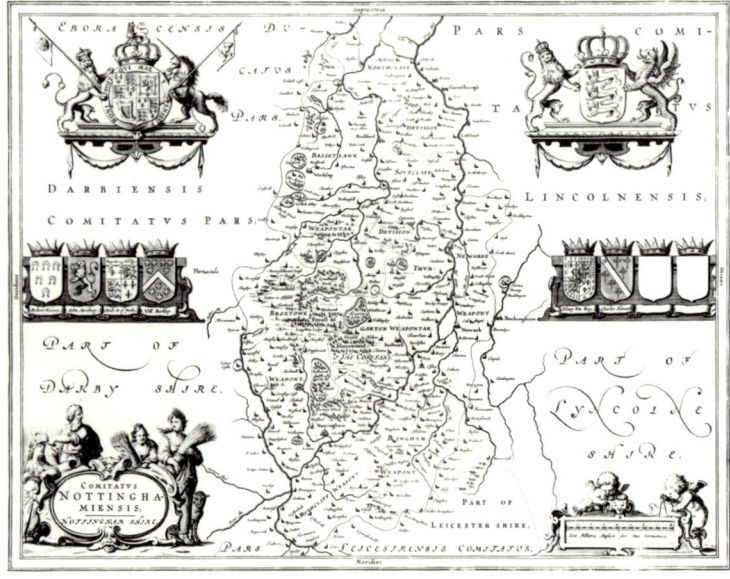

Notes Central on the map is Sherwood Forest, famous from the tales of Robin Hood. The title cartouche decoration is decorated with images of the production of grain. The coats of arms of the earls of Nottingham are drawn on sides of the map. The map has been copied from Speed's *Theatre*, edition after 1623, or from the copy of it in Janssonius' Appendix of 1644, and was specially made for the atlas of England, which Joan Blaeu in 1645 joined as a fourth part to his *Atlas novus*.

Occurrence in atlases   2:301 Theatrum Orbis Terrarum sive Atlas Novus Pars Quarta, J. Blaeu, 1646: 30 5A 297-298

2:302-3 Theatrum Orbis Terrarum sive Atlas Novus Pars Quarta, J. Blaeu, 1646-48: 30 4Q 259-260

2:311 Le Theatre du Monde ou Nouvel Atlas, Quatriesme Partie, J. Blaeu: 30 4L 153-154

2:312 Cinquème Volume de la Geographie Blaviane, J. Blaeu, 1663-67: 30 4E 215-216

2:321 Toonneel des Aerdycks oft Nieuwe Atlas... Vierde deel, J. Blaeu, 1648: 30 4X 281-282

2:322 Toonneel des Aerdycks oft Nieuwe Atlas... Vierde deel, J. Blaeu, 1648: 30 4I 239-240

2:331 Novus Atlas and Atlas Major (Vierter Teil), J. Blaeu, 1645-48: 30 5B 291-292

Nuevo Atlas del Reyno de Inglaterra, J. Blaeu, 1645/48: 30 4X 275-276

References   Van der Krogt 2002 18:43.

128.1 [5340:1.1] Derbyshire
COMITATVS | DARBIEN- | SIS
The county of Derby
38 x 49 cm.

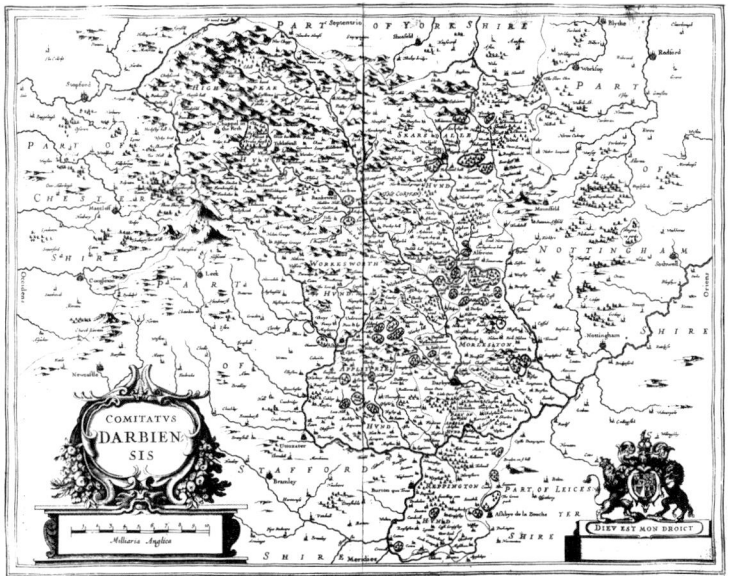

Notes   On the bottom right is the royal coat of arms. Underneath is the motto of the British monarch: 'Dieu et mon droit', which means God and my right.

Occurrence in atlases
1:432 Des Nieuwen Atlantis Aenhang, Janssonius, 1644: 8 h
1:434/36 Nieuwen Atlas... Het Vierde deel, Janssonius, 1647-49/1658: v4 28 3D

128.2 [5340:1.2] Derbyshire
COMITATVS | DARBIEN- | SIS
The county of Derby

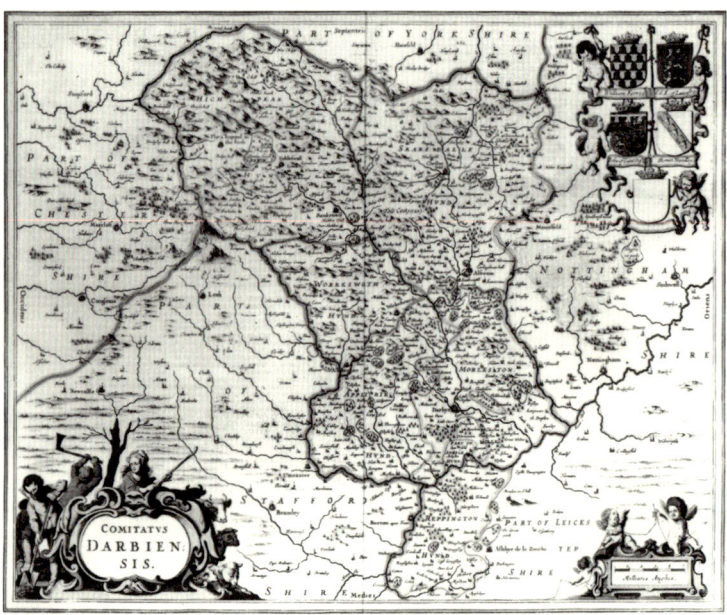

Notes   A new cartouche is added, oval shaped and surrounded by images of a man digging, a man cutting wood and a woman herding cattle; at the top right are coats of arms.

Occurrence in atlases

1:403/05 Atlas Novus, Janssonius, 1647/1657-62: v4 28 4H 233-234

1:414/15 Le Nouvel Atlas... Tome Quatrieme, Janssonius, 1646-49: v4 28 4O 251-252

1:425 Novus Atlas, Janssonius, 1647-49: v4 28 5A 297-298

1:434/36 Nieuwen Atlas... Het Vierde deel, Janssonius, 1647-49/1658: v4 28 3D

1:408 Atlas, Janssonius, after c. 1680: v3 27

129   [5340:2] Derbyshire
DARBIENSIS | COMITATVS. | Vernacule | DARBIE SHIRE
The county of Derby, vernacularly Derbyshire
38 x 49.5 cm.

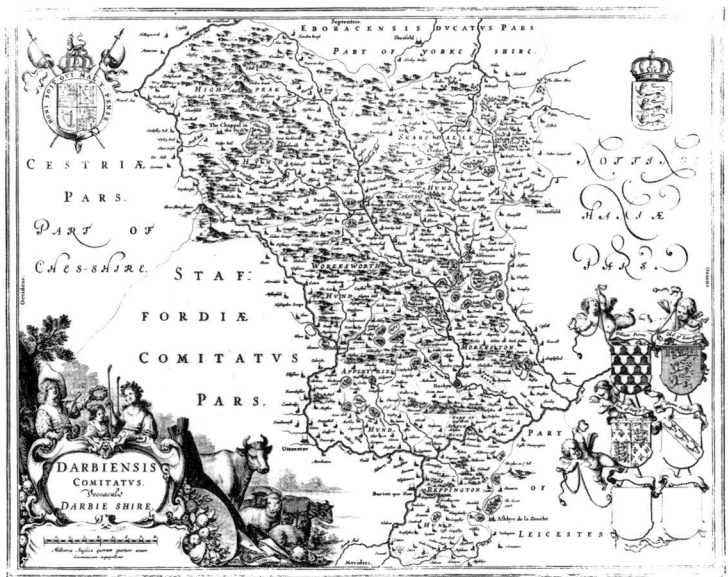

Notes   The shepherds and the cattle decorating the title cartouche show that the county was well known for its cultivation of livestock. The royal coat of arms, the coat of arms of England and the coats of arms of the earls of Derby decorate the other corners of the map. The map has been copied from Speed's *Theatre*, edition after 1623, and is specially made for the atlas of England, which Joan Blaeu in 1645 joined as a fourth part to his *Atlas novus*.

Occurrence in atlases   2:301 Theatrum Orbis Terrarum sive Atlas Novus Pars Quarta, J. Blaeu, 1646: 31 5C 301-302
2:302-3 Theatrum Orbis Terrarum sive Atlas Novus Pars Quarta, J. Blaeu, 1646-48: 31 4R 261-262
2:311 Le Theatre du Monde ou Nouvel Atlas, Quatriesme Partie, J. Blaeu: 31 4M 155-256
2:312 Cinquème Volume de la Geographie Blaviane, J. Blaeu, 1663-67: 31 4F 217-218
2:321 Toonneel des Aerdycks oft Nieuwe Atlas... Vierde deel, J. Blaeu, 1648: 31 4Y 283-284
2:322 Toonneel des Aerdycks oft Nieuwe Atlas... Vierde deel, J. Blaeu, 1648: 31 4K 241-242
2:331 Novus Atlas and Atlas Major (Vierter Teil), J. Blaeu, 1645-48: 31 5C 293-294
Nuevo Atlas del Reyno de Inglaterra, J. Blaeu, 1645/48: 31 4Y 277-278

References   Van der Krogt 2002 18:44.

130   [5340:373] Derbyshire
        DERBIENSIS | Comitatus
        Derbyshire
        Petrus Kærius Cælavit.
        8.5 x 12 cm.

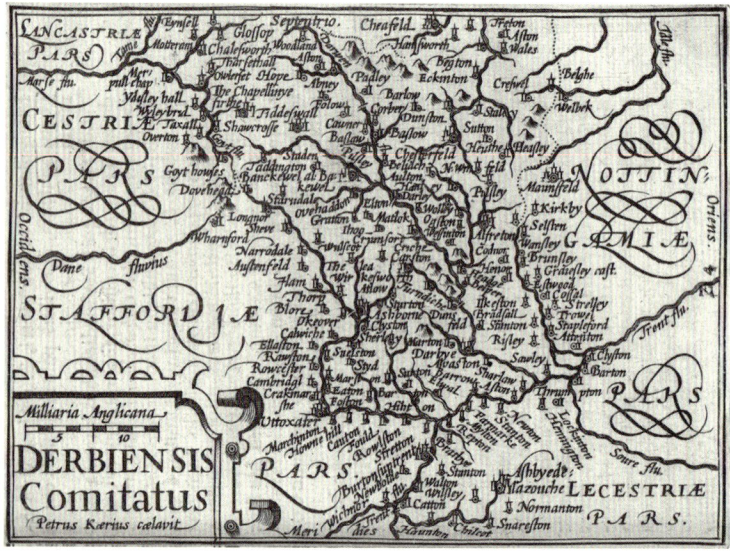

Notes   This map is from a collection of 44 maps of the British Isles, engraved by Pieter van den Keere. The maps are comparable in size to those of the *Tabularum Geographicarum*, published by Pieter Bertius, for which Van den Keere engraved many maps. Although the maps of Van den Keere form one collection, no title-page is known.

Occurrence in atlases
373:01 Atlas of the British Isles, Van den Keere, c. 1605: 17
373:02 Britannia, Camden, 1617: 17 Z4r 359

References   Skelton 1970, 4.

131   [5345:1] Worcestershire and Warwickshire
WIGORNIENSIS | Comitatus cum | WARWICENSI; | nec non |
CONVENTRIÆ LIBERTAS
Worcestershire en Warwickshire, also the jurisdiction of Coventry
Amstelodami | Apud Ioannem Ianßonium
43 x 52 cm.

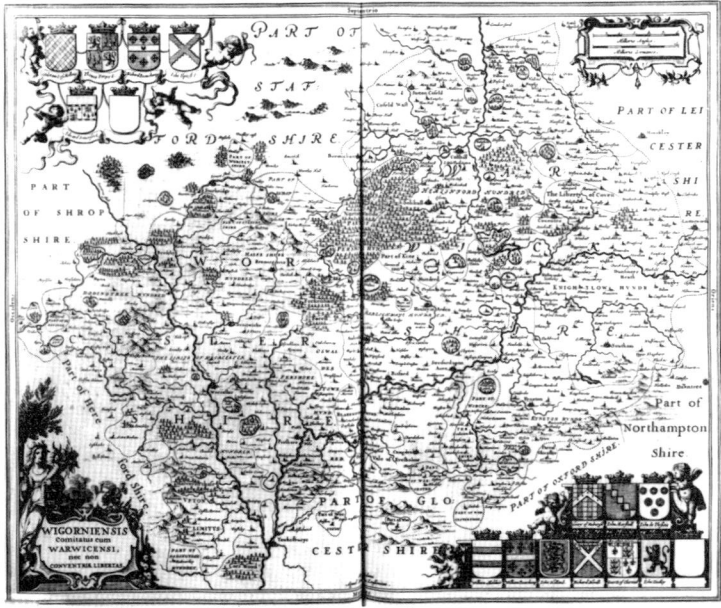

Notes   Above left and below right there are some coats of arms of noble families.
The title cartouche is surrounded by a rural scene.

Occurrence in atlases
1:403/05 Atlas Novus, Janssonius, 1647/1657-62: v4 29 4K 237-238
1:414/15 Le Nouvel Atlas... Tome Quatrieme, Janssonius, 1646-49: v4 29 4Q 255-256
1:425 Novus Atlas, Janssonius, 1647-49: v4 29 5C 301-302
1:434/36 Nieuwen Atlas... Het Vierde deel, Janssonius, 1647-49/1658: v4 29 3E 143-144
1:408 Atlas, Janssonius, after c. 1680: v3 28

132   [5345:2] Worcestershire and Warwickshire
       **WIGORNIENSIS | Comitatus et Comitatus | WARWICENSIS; |
       nec non | COVENTRÆ LIBERTAS. | WORCESTER, WARWIK
       SHIRE. | and THE LIBERTY OF COVENTRE**
       Worcestershire en Warwickshire, also the jurisdiction of Coventry
       41 X 50 cm.

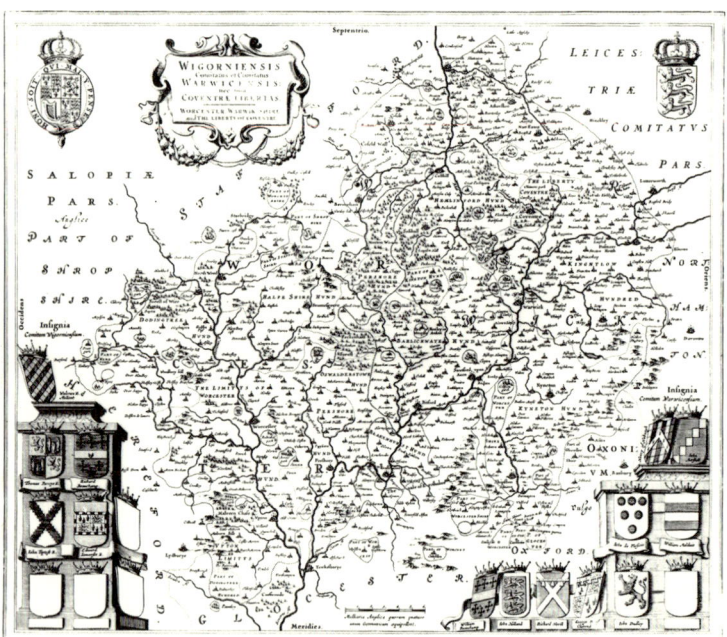

Notes   The four corners of the map have been decorated with coats of arms. In
the corners at the top are the royal coat of arms and the English coat of arms, and
in the corners underneath are the coats of arms of the earls of Worcester and of
Warwick. The map has been copied from Speed's *Theatre*, edition after 1623, and
was specially made for the atlas of England, which Joan Blaeu in 1645 joined as a
fourth part to his *Atlas novus*.

Occurrence in atlases

2:301 Theatrum Orbis Terrarum sive Atlas Novus Pars Quarta, J. Blaeu, 1646: 32
5E 305-306

2:302-3 Theatrum Orbis Terrarum sive Atlas Novus Pars Quarta, J. Blaeu, 1646-
48: 32 4T 265-266

2:311 Le Theatre du Monde ou Nouvel Atlas, Quatriesme Partie, J. Blaeu: 32 4N
257-258

2:312 Cinquème Volume de la Geographie Blaviane, J. Blaeu, 1663-67: 32 4G 219-
220

2:321 Toonneel des Aerdycks oft Nieuwe Atlas... Vierde deel, J. Blaeu, 1648: 32
5A 287-288

2:322 Toonneel des Aerdycks oft Nieuwe Atlas... Vierde deel, J. Blaeu, 1648: 32
4M 245-246
2:331 Novus Atlas and Atlas Major (Vierter Teil), J. Blaeu, 1645-48: 32 5E 297-
298
Nuevo Atlas del Reyno de Inglaterra, J. Blaeu, 1645/48: 32 5A 281-282

References   Van der Krogt 2002 18:45.

133   [5345:373] **Worcestershire**
       Wigornien | sis comitatus.
       The county of Worcester
       8.5 x 12 cm.

Notes   This map shows England, Scotland and Ireland. At the corner left above there is a coat of arms of the British monarch. Above right, there is an inset map of the Orkney Islands.

Occurrence in atlases
373:01 Atlas of the British Isles, Van den Keere, c. 1605: 25
373:02 Britannia, Camden, 1617: 19 2A4v 376

References   Skelton 1970, 4.

134   [5350:2] Staffordshire
STAFFORDIENSIS | COMITATVS; | Vulgo | STAFFORD SHIRE
The county of Stafford, in the vulgar tongue Staffordshire
41 x 50 cm.

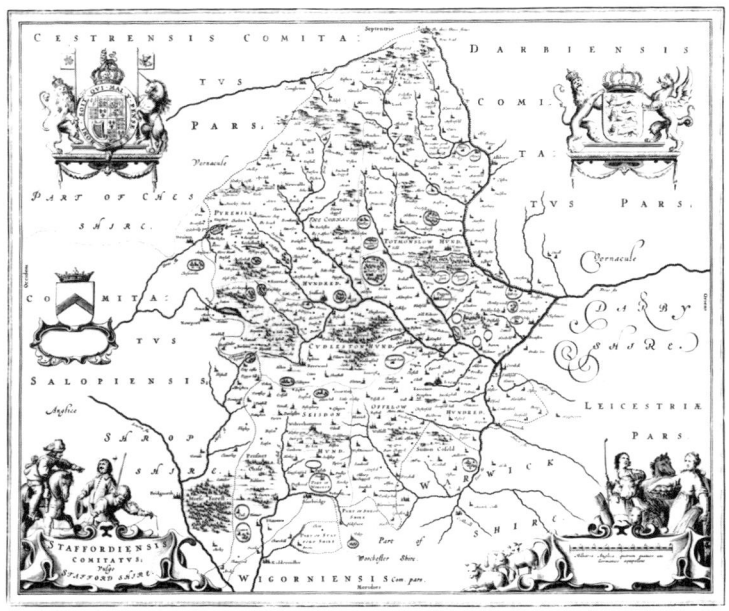

Notes   At the scale cartouche, a shepherd with sheep and a country-woman with grain and fruit are drawn. An empty cartouche was possibly intended for a dedication. Above this empty cartouche is the coat of arms of Stafford. The map has been copied from Speed's *Theatre*, edition after 1623, and was specially made for the atlas of England, which Joan Blaeu in 1645 joined as a fourth part to his *Atlas novus*.

Occurrence in atlases   2:301 Theatrum Orbis Terrarum sive Atlas Novus Pars
    Quarta, J. Blaeu, 1646: 33 5H 315-316
2:302-3 Theatrum Orbis Terrarum sive Atlas Novus Pars Quarta, J. Blaeu, 1646-48: 33 4Y 273-274
2:311 Le Theatre du Monde ou Nouvel Atlas, Quatriesme Partie, J. Blaeu: 33 4Q 267-268
2:312 Cinquème Volume de la Geographie Blaviane, J. Blaeu, 1663-67: 33 4K 227-228
2:321 Toonneel des Aerdycks oft Nieuwe Atlas... Vierde deel, J. Blaeu, 1648: 33 5D 297-298
2:322 Toonneel des Aerdycks oft Nieuwe Atlas... Vierde deel, J. Blaeu, 1648: 33 4P 253-254
2:331 Novus Atlas and Atlas Major (Vierter Teil), J. Blaeu, 1645-48: 33 5H 307-308
Nuevo Atlas del Reyno de Inglaterra, J. Blaeu, 1645/48: 33 5E 293-294

References   Van der Krogt 2002 18:46.

135   [5350:373] Staffordshire
       Staffordia
       Staffordshire
       P. Kærius cælavit.
       8.5 x 12 cm.

Notes   This map is from a collection of 44 maps of the British Isles, engraved by
Pieter van den Keere. The maps are comparable in size to those of the *Tabularum
Geographicarum*, published by Pieter Bertius, for which Van den Keere engraved
many maps. Although the maps of Van den Keere form one collection, no title-
page is known.

Occurrence in atlases
373:01 Atlas of the British Isles, Van den Keere, c. 1605: 24
373:02 Britannia, Camden, 1617: 20 2A8r 383

References   Skelton 1970, 4.

136   [5355:1] Shropshire
SALOPIENSIS | COMITATVS | cum STAFFORDIENSI. |
SHROPSHIRE & | STAFFORDSHIRE
Shropshire with Staffordshire.
42.5 X 53.5 cm.

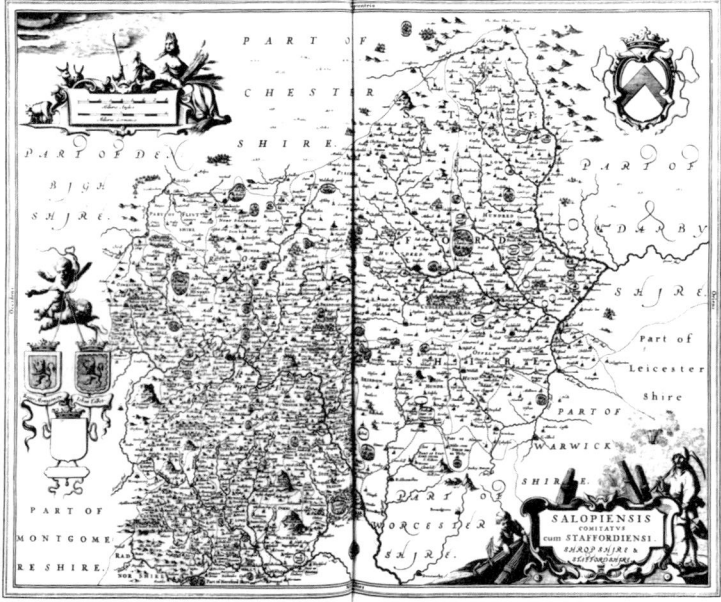

Notes   Above right is the coat of arms of Stafford. Left of the map there are some
coats of arms of noble families, one of which is empty.

Occurrence in atlases
1:403/05 Atlas Novus, Janssonius, 1647/1657-62: v4 30 4N 245-246
1:414/15 Le Nouvel Atlas... Tome Quatrieme, Janssonius, 1646-49: v4 30 4T 263-264
1:425 Novus Atlas, Janssonius, 1647-49: v4 30 5F 311-312
1:434/36 Nieuwen Atlas... Het Vierde deel, Janssonius, 1647-49/1658: v4 30 3G
147-148
1:408 Atlas, Janssonius, after c. 1680: v3 29

137   [5355:2] Shropshire
COMITATVS | SALOPIENSIS; | Anglice | SHROP SHIRE
In English Shropshire
38 x 49.5 cm.

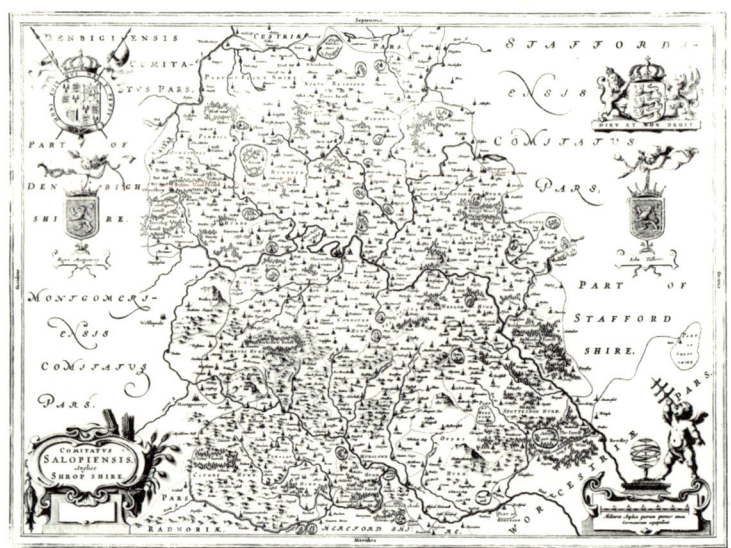

Notes   The coats of arms on this map belong to the king of England, to Roger of Montgomery, the first known earl of Shrewsbury (1022–1094), and to John Talbot, earl of Shrewsbury at the time of production of this map in 1645. The putto on the scale cartouche observes the sky with a Jacob's staff. This is especially an instrument for navigation at sea, which makes it remarkable on a map of an inland county with no coastline. The map has been copied from Speed's *Theatre*, edition after 1623, and was specially made for the atlas of England, which Joan Blaeu in 1645 joined as a fourth part to his *Atlas novus*.

Occurrence in atlases   2:301 Theatrum Orbis Terrarum sive Atlas Novus Pars Quarta, J. Blaeu, 1646: 34 5K 321-322
2:302-3 Theatrum Orbis Terrarum sive Atlas Novus Pars Quarta, J. Blaeu, 1646-48: 34 5A 277-278
2:311 Le Theatre du Monde ou Nouvel Atlas, Quatriesme Partie, J. Blaeu: 34 4R 269
2:312 Cinquème Volume de la Geographie Blaviane, J. Blaeu, 1663-67: 34 4L 229-230
2:321 Toonneel des Aerdrycks oft Nieuwe Atlas... Vierde deel, J. Blaeu, 1648: 34 5E 299-300
2:322 Toonneel des Aerdrycks oft Nieuwe Atlas... Vierde deel, J. Blaeu, 1648: 34 4R 257-258
2:331 Novus Atlas and Atlas Major (Vierter Teil), J. Blaeu, 1645-48: 34 5K 311-312
Nuevo Atlas del Reyno de Inglaterra, J. Blaeu, 1645/48: 34 5G 297-298

References   Van der Krogt 2002 18:47.

138   [5355:373] Shropshire
SALOPIA
Shropshire
Petrus Kærius Cælavit.
8.5 x 12 cm.

Notes   This map shows England, Scotland and Ireland. At the corner left above there is a coat of arms of the British monarch. Above right, there is an inset map of the Orkney Islands.

Occurrence in atlases
373:01 Atlas of the British Isles, Van den Keere, c. 1605: 23
373:02 Britannia, Camden, 1617: 21 2B3v 390

References   Skelton 1970, 4.

139.1 [5360:1.1] Cheshire
**THE | COVNTYE PALATINE | OF | CHESTER | Comitatus |
CESTRENSIS**
The Palatine County of Chester. The County of Chester
Amstelodami Apud Ioannem Ianßonium
38 x 50 cm.

Notes   Cheshire's name was originally derived from an early name for Cheshire,
and was first recorded as Legeceasterscir in the Anglo-Saxon Chronicles, meaning
the shire of the city of legions. Cheshire in the Domesday Book was recorded as
a larger county than it is today. It included two hundreds, Atiscross and Exestan,
that later became part of Wales.

Occurrence in atlases
1:324 Appendix Atlantis, Janssonius, 1636: 16 P
1:323 Newer Atlas, Janssonius, 1636: vi 20 S(P)
1:332 Appendix Atlantis, Janssonius/Hondius, 1637: 14 S
1:421/2 Newer Atlas, Janssonius, 1638: vi 19 P
1:431 Nieuwen Atlas, Janssonius, 1638-44: vi 18 Z(S)

139.2 [5360:1.2] Cheshire
CESTRIA | COMITATVS | PALATINVS. | THE COUNTYE |
PALATINE OF | CHESTER
The county palatine of Chester
38 x 50 cm.

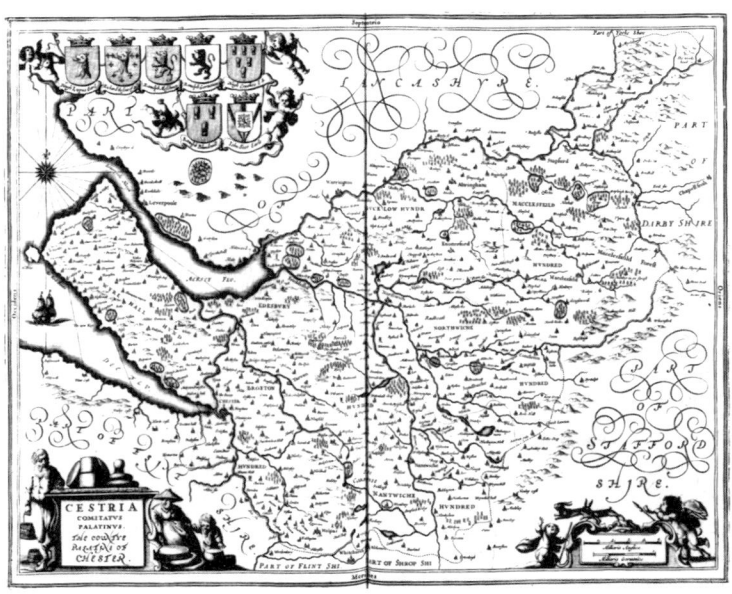

Notes On the left of the map are the coats of arms of seven noble families.

Occurrence in atlases

1:403/05 Atlas Novus, Janssonius, 1647/1657-62: v4 31 4Q 253-254
1:414/15 Le Nouvel Atlas... Tome Quatrieme, Janssonius, 1646-49: v4 31 4Y 271-272
1:425 Novus Atlas, Janssonius, 1647-49: v4 31 5I 321-322
1:434/36 Nieuwen Atlas... Het Vierde deel, Janssonius, 1647-49/1658: v4 31 3I 151-152
1:408 Atlas, Janssonius, after c. 1680: v3 30

140   [5360:2] Cheshire
CESTRIA | COMITATVS | PALATINVS
The county palatine of Chester
38 x 50 cm.

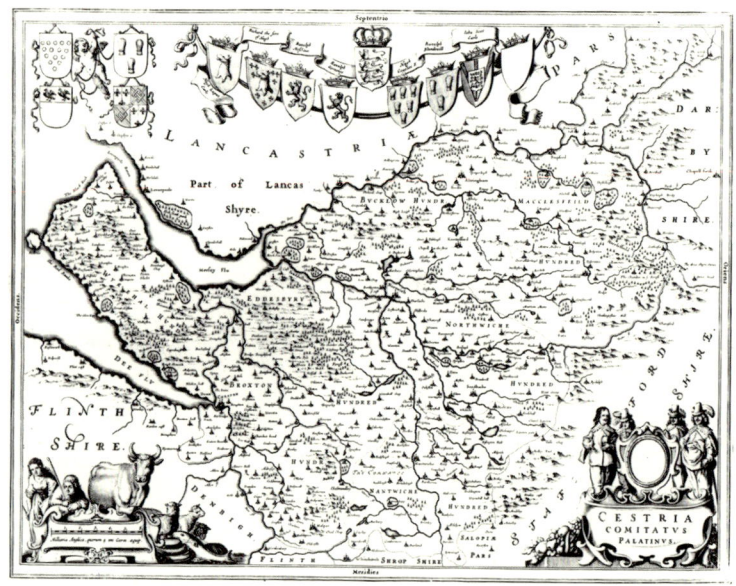

Notes   At the top are the coats of arms of the earls of Chester. The map has been copied from Speed's *Theatre*, edition after 1623, and was specially made for the atlas of England, which Joan Blaeu in 1645 joined as a fourth part to his *Atlas novus*.

Occurrence in atlases

2:301 Theatrum Orbis Terrarum sive Atlas Novus Pars Quarta, J. Blaeu, 1646: 35 5M 327-328

2:302-3 Theatrum Orbis Terrarum sive Atlas Novus Pars Quarta, J. Blaeu, 1646-48: 35 5C 283-284

2:311 Le Theatre du Monde ou Nouvel Atlas, Quatriesme Partie, J. Blaeu: 35 4T 275-276

2:312 Cinquème Volume de la Geographie Blaviane, J. Blaeu, 1663-67: 35 4N 233-234

2:321 Toonneel des Aerdycks oft Nieuwe Atlas... Vierde deel, J. Blaeu, 1648: 35 5G 305-306

2:322 Toonneel des Aerdycks oft Nieuwe Atlas... Vierde deel, J. Blaeu, 1648: 35 4T 261-262

2:331 Novus Atlas and Atlas Major (Vierter Teil), J. Blaeu, 1645-48: 35 5M 317-318

Nuevo Atlas del Reyno de Inglaterra, J. Blaeu, 1645/48: 35 5K 305-306

References   Van der Krogt 2002 18:48.

141 [5360:373] Cheshire
CESTRIAE
Cheshire
Petrus | Kærius cælavit.
8.5 x 12 cm.

Notes This map is from a collection of 44 maps of the British Isles, engraved by Pieter van den Keere. The maps are comparable in size to those of the *Tabularum Geographicarum*, published by Pieter Bertius, for which Van den Keere engraved many maps. Although the maps of Van den Keere form one collection, no title-page is known.

Occurrence in atlases
373:01 Atlas of the British Isles, Van den Keere, c. 1605: 22
373:02 Britannia, Camden, 1617: 22 2B8v 400

References Skelton 1970, 4.

142.1 [5365:1.1] Yorkshire
PROVINCIA | EBORACEN- | SIS. | YORKE-SHIRE
The Province of York. Yorkshire
Amstelodami Apud Ioan: Ianßonium
38 x 50 cm.

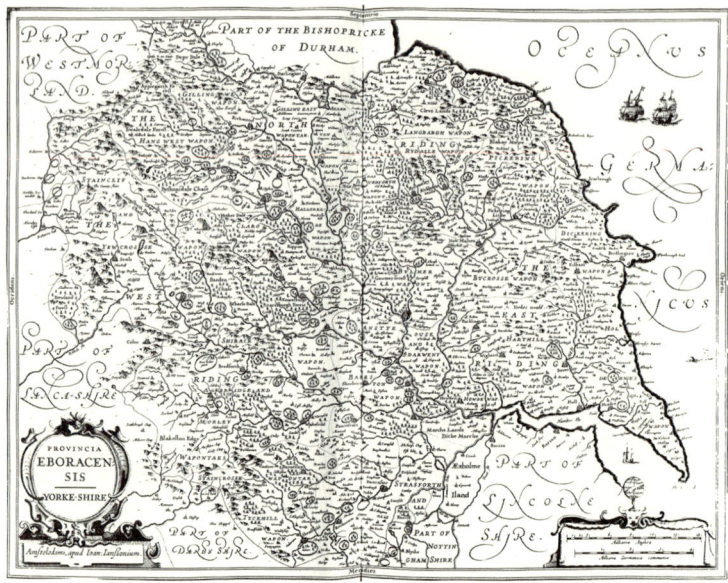

Notes   The county of Yorkshire was so named as it is the shire (administrative area or county) of the City of York or York's shire. York is derived from the Latin name for the city, Eboracum. 'Shire' is from Old English *scir*, and appears to be allied to shear as it is a division of the land.

Occurrence in atlases

1:324 Appendix Atlantis, Janssonius, 1636: 18 R
1:323 Newer Atlas, Janssonius, 1636: vi 22 V(R)
1:332 Appendix Atlantis, Janssonius/Hondius, 1637: 16 V
1:421/2 Newer Atlas, Janssonius, 1638: vi 21 R
1:431 Nieuwen Atlas, Janssonius, 1638-44: vi 20 2B(V)

142.2 [5365:1.2] Yorkshire
DVCATVS | EBORACEN- | SIS. | Anglice | YORKSHIRE
The duchy of York. English Yorkshire

Notes   In the sixteenth and seventeenth centuries Leeds and other towns centred on the wool industry continued to grow, along with Huddersfield, Hull and Sheffield, while coal mining first came into prominence in the West Riding of Yorkshire. Canals and turnpike roads were introduced in the late 1700s. In the following century the spa towns of Harrogate and Scarborough also flourished, due to people believing mineral water had curing properties.

Occurrence in atlases
1:403/05 Atlas Novus, Janssonius, 1647/1657-62: v4 39 5H 291-292
1:414/15 Le Nouvel Atlas... Tome Quatrieme, Janssonius, 1646-49: v4 39 5O 309-310
1:425 Novus Atlas, Janssonius, 1647-49: v4 39 6B 363-364
1:434/36 Nieuwen Atlas... Het Vierde deel, Janssonius, 1647-49/1658: v4 39 3N 159-160
1:408 Atlas, Janssonius, after c. 1680: v3 38

143   [5365:2] Yorkshire
DVCATVS | EBORACENSIS | Anglice | YORK SHIRE
The duchy of York. English Yorkshire
39 X 50 cm.

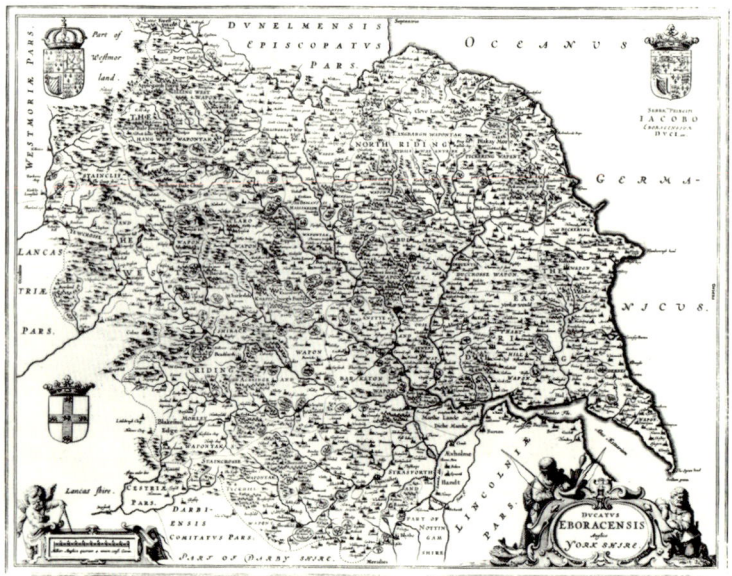

Notes   At the top corner is the coat of arms of James, duke of York (1633–1701), the third son of Charles II, who became duke of York in 1644 and succeeded his brother in 1685 as King James II of England. The two other coats of arms are of the monarch and of the duchy. The map has been copied from Speed's *Theatre*, edition after 1623, and is specially made for the atlas of England, which Joan Blaeu in 1645 joined as a fourth part to his *Atlas novus*.

Occurrence in atlases   2:301 Theatrum Orbis Terrarum sive Atlas Novus Pars Quarta, J. Blaeu, 1646: 47 6I 371-372
2:302-3 Theatrum Orbis Terrarum sive Atlas Novus Pars Quarta, J. Blaeu, 1646-48: 47 5X 321-322
2:311 Le Theatre du Monde ou Nouvel Atlas, Quatriesme Partie, J. Blaeu: 47 5N 317-318
2:312 Cinquème Volume de la Geographie Blaviane, J. Blaeu, 1663-67: 47 5G 267-268
2:321 Toonneel des Aerdycks oft Nieuwe Atlas... Vierde deel, J. Blaeu, 1648: 47 6B 345-346
2:322 Toonneel des Aerdycks oft Nieuwe Atlas... Vierde deel, J. Blaeu, 1648: 47 5N 297-298
2:331 Novus Atlas and Atlas Major (Vierter Teil), J. Blaeu, 1645-48: 47 6H 401
Nuevo Atlas del Reyno de Inglaterra, J. Blaeu, 1645/48: 47 6I 355-356

References   Van der Krogt 2002 18:60.

144.1   [5365:352.1] Yorkshire
EBORACENSIS | PROVINCIA
The Province of York
Petrus Kærius Cælavit.
16 x 21 cm.

Notes   The nineteenth century saw Yorkshire's continued economic growth, with the population growing and the Industrial Revolution continuing with prominent industries in coal, textiles and steel (especially in Sheffield).

Occurrence in atlases

352:32/33 Atlas Minor, Janssonius, 1648-51: VI 12 F4r 47

144.2 [5365:352.2] Yorkshire
Comté | D'YORCK.
The county of York

Notes This map appeared in the *Atlas soulagé de son gros & pesant fardeau*, pub-lished by Pieter van der Aa. Almost all the maps are printed from reworked plates of Janssonius's *Atlas Minor*. The titles and scale were translated into French. Several Latin texts on the maps have been removed, as have the Latin names of the wind directions in the borders. The cartouches have been modernized and win-droses added. Other modernizations are the removal of ships and sea monsters, and erasing names in curled letters and replacing them with Roman type letters. Latin names of seas and countries are often translated into French.

Occurrence in atlases
352:51.2-9 Atlas soulagé..., Van der Aa, c. 1714: v4 13 blank

145   [5366:1] Yorkshire (West)
DVCATVS | EBORACENSIS | PARS OCCIDENTALIS; | THE
WESTRIDING OF | YORKE SHIRE
The western part of the duchy of York; the West Riding of Yorkshire
42 x 50 cm.

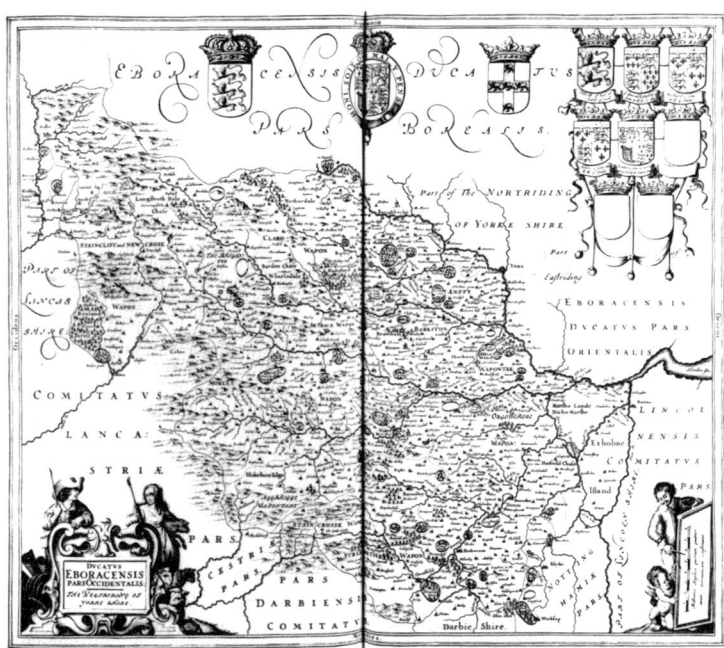

Notes   In the middle above is the royal coat of arms. The motto in the coat is:
Honi soit qui mal y pense, which means 'Shame be to him who thinks evil of it',
the motto of the Order of the Garter. Left of this is the coat of arms of England.

Occurrence in atlases
1:403/05 Atlas Novus, Janssonius, 1647/1657-62: v4 40 5I 293-294
1:414/15 Le Nouvel Atlas... Tome Quatrieme, Janssonius, 1646-49: v4 40 5P 311-
312
1:425 Novus Atlas, Janssonius, 1647-49: v4 40 6C 365-366
1:434/36 Nieuwen Atlas... Het Vierde deel, Janssonius, 1647-49/1658: v4 40 3O2
1:408 Atlas, Janssonius, after c. 1680: v3 39

146   [5366:2] Yorkshire (West)
        DVCATVS | EBORACENSIS | PARS OCCIDENTALIS; | THE
        WESTRIDING OF | YORKE SHIRE
        The western part of the duchy of York; the West Riding of Yorkshire
        38.5 x 50 cm.

Notes   The map is decorated with the coats of arms of England, the king, the
duchy and the earls and dukes of York. The map has been copied from Speed's
Theatre, edition after 1623, and was specially made for the atlas of England, which
Joan Blaeu in 1645 joined as a fourth part to his *Atlas novus*.

Occurrence in atlases

2:301 Theatrum Orbis Terrarum sive Atlas Novus Pars Quarta, J. Blaeu, 1646: 48
6K 373-374

2:302-3 Theatrum Orbis Terrarum sive Atlas Novus Pars Quarta, J. Blaeu, 1646-
48: 48 5Y 323-324

2:311 Le Theatre du Monde ou Nouvel Atlas, Quatriesme Partie, J. Blaeu: 48 5O
319-320

2:312 Cinquème Volume de la Geographie Blaviane, J. Blaeu, 1663-67: 48 5H 269-270

2:321 Toonneel des Aerdycks oft Nieuwe Atlas... Vierde deel, J. Blaeu, 1648: 48
6C 347-348

2:322 Toonneel des Aerdycks oft Nieuwe Atlas... Vierde deel, J. Blaeu, 1648: 48
5O 299-300

2:331 Novus Atlas and Atlas Major (Vierter Teil), J. Blaeu, 1645-48: 48 6I 403-404
Nuevo Atlas del Reyno de Inglaterra, J. Blaeu, 1645/48: 48 6K 357-358

References   Van der Krogt 2002 18:61.

147   [5367:1] Yorkshire (East)
DVCATVS | EBORACENSIS | PARS ORIENTALIS. | THE
EASTRIDING of | YORKE SHIRE
The eastern part of the duchy of York. The East Riding of Yorkshire
38 x 50 cm.

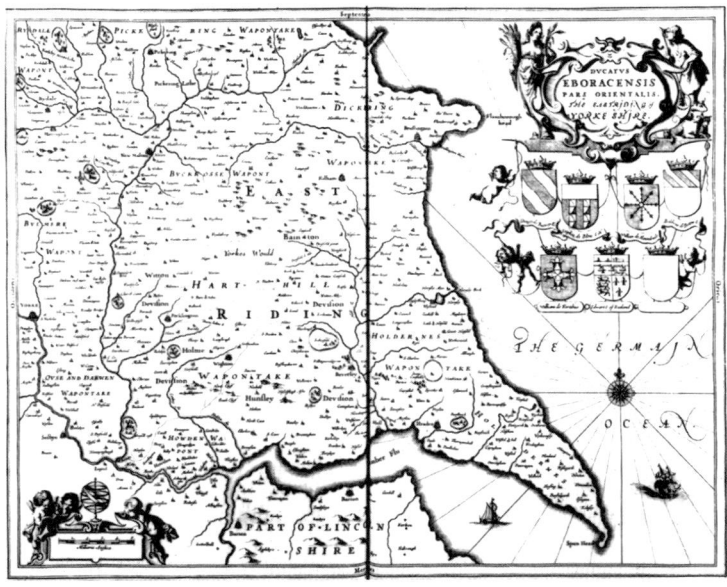

Notes   Beneath the title cartouche there are seven coats of arms of noble families,
of which one is empty.

Occurrence in atlases
1:403/05 Atlas Novus, Janssonius, 1647/1657-62: v4 41 5M 301-302
1:414/15 Le Nouvel Atlas... Tome Quatrieme, Janssonius, 1646-49: v4 41 5S 319-
320
1:425 Novus Atlas, Janssonius, 1647-49: v4 41 6F 375-376
1:434/36 Nieuwen Atlas... Het Vierde deel, Janssonius, 1647-49/1658: v4 41 3O3
1:408 Atlas, Janssonius, after c. 1680: v3 40

148   [5367:2] Yorkshire (East)
       DVCATVS | EBORACENSIS | PARS ORIENTALIS; | The Eastrid-
       ing of Yorkeshire
       The eastern part of the duchy of York; the East Riding of Yorkshire
       38 x 50 cm.

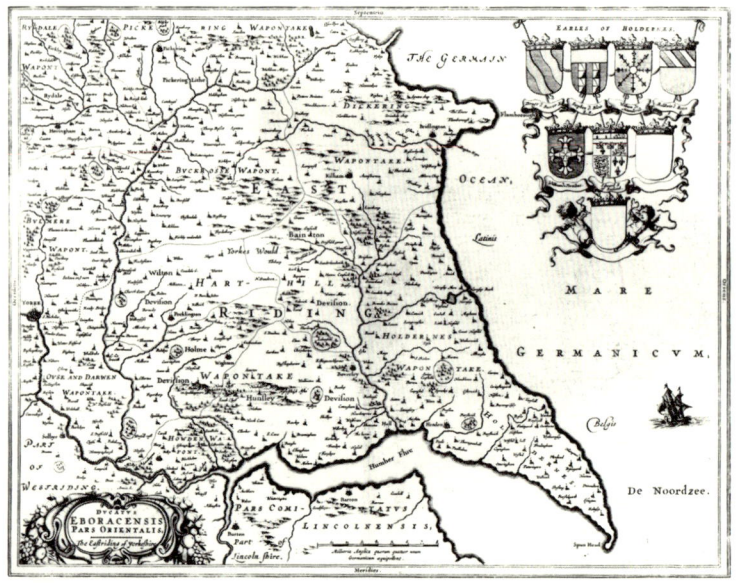

Notes   The map is decorated with the coats of arms of the earls of Holderness. The map has been copied from Speed's *Theatre*, edition after 1623, and was specially made for the atlas of England, which Joan Blaeu in 1645 joined as a fourth part to his *Atlas novus*.

Occurrence in atlases

2:301 Theatrum Orbis Terrarum sive Atlas Novus Pars Quarta, J. Blaeu, 1646: 49 6N 383-384

2:302-3 Theatrum Orbis Terrarum sive Atlas Novus Pars Quarta, J. Blaeu, 1646-48: 49 6B 331-332

2:311 Le Theatre du Monde ou Nouvel Atlas, Quatriesme Partie, J. Blaeu: 49 5R 327-328

2:312 Cinquème Volume de la Geographie Blaviane, J. Blaeu, 1663-67: 49 5K 275-276

2:321 Toonneel des Aerdycks oft Nieuwe Atlas... Vierde deel, J. Blaeu, 1648: 49 6F 357-358

2:322 Toonneel des Aerdycks oft Nieuwe Atlas... Vierde deel, J. Blaeu, 1648: 49 5Q 305-306

2:331 Novus Atlas and Atlas Major (Vierter Teil), J. Blaeu, 1645-48: 49 6M 413-414

Nuevo Atlas del Reyno de Inglaterra, J. Blaeu, 1645/48: 49 6O 369-370

References   Van der Krogt 2002 18:62.

149   [5368:1] Yorkshireshire (North)
DVCATVS | EBORACENSIS | PARS BOREALIS. | THE
NORTHRIDINGE of | YORKESHIRE
The northern part of the duchy of York. The North Riding of Yorkshire
38.5 x 49 cm.

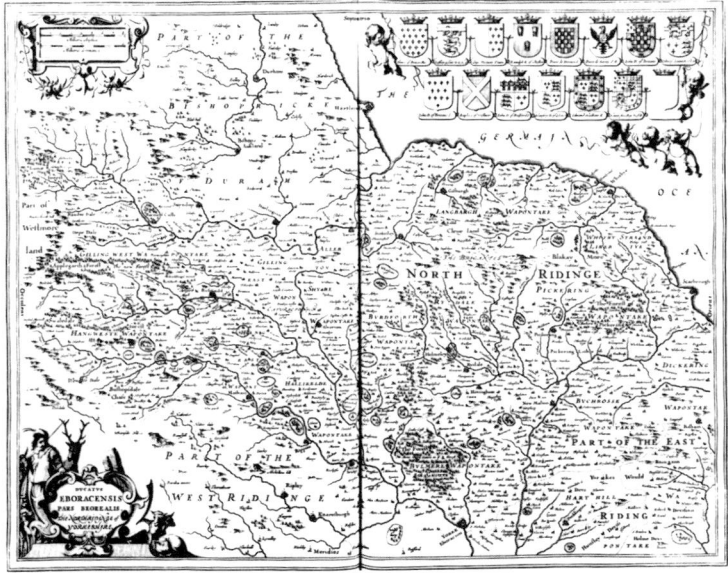

Notes   Above right there are fifteen coats of arms of noble families, surrounded
by putti.

Occurrence in atlases
1:403/05 Atlas Novus, Janssonius, 1647/1657-62: v4 42 5O 305-306
1:414/15 Le Nouvel Atlas... Tome Quatrieme, Janssonius, 1646-49: v4 42 5T 321-
1:425 Novus Atlas, Janssonius, 1647-49: v4 42 6H 379-380
1:434/36 Nieuwen Atlas... Het Vierde deel, Janssonius, 1647-49/1658: v4 42 3O4
1:408 Atlas, Janssonius, after c. 1680: v3 41

150 [5368:2] Yorkshire (North)
DVCATVS | EBORACENSIS | PARS BOREALIS | THE NORTH-RIDING | OF YORK SHIRE
The northern part of the duchy of York. The North Riding of Yorkshire
38 x 50 cm.

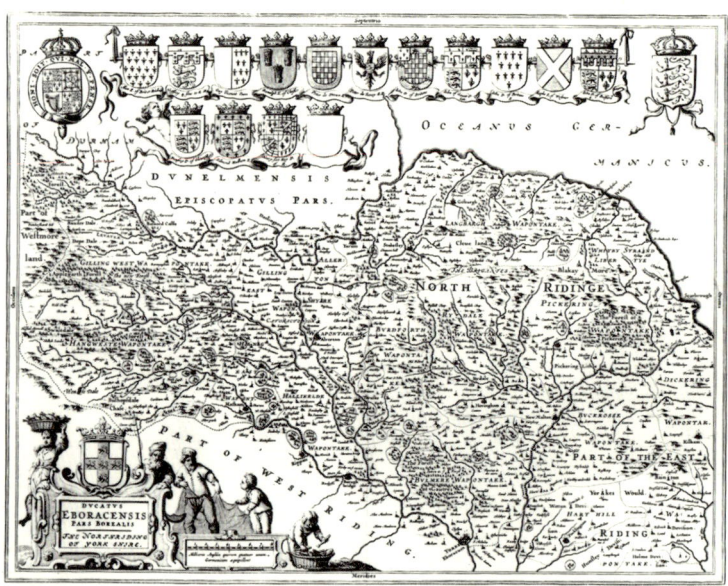

Notes The title cartouche is decorated with images of fishermen and fish. At the top corners are the coats of arms of the king and of England and the coats of arms of the earls of York. The map has been copied to the card of East and North Riding from Speed's *Theatre*, edition by 1623, and was specially made for the atlas of England, which Joan Blaeu in 1645 joined as a fourth part to his *Atlas novus*.

Occurrence in atlases 2:301 Theatrum Orbis Terrarum sive Atlas Novus Pars Quarta, J. Blaeu, 1646: 50 6P 387-388
2:302-3 Theatrum Orbis Terrarum sive Atlas Novus Pars Quarta, J. Blaeu, 1646-48: 50 6D 335-336
2:311 Le Theatre du Monde ou Nouvel Atlas, Quatriesme Partie, J. Blaeu: 50 5S 329-330
2:312 Cinquème Volume de la Geographie Blaviane, J. Blaeu, 1663-67: 50 5L 277-278
2:321 Toonneel des Aerdycks oft Nieuwe Atlas... Vierde deel, J. Blaeu, 1648: 50 6H 361-362
2:322 Toonneel des Aerdycks oft Nieuwe Atlas... Vierde deel, J. Blaeu, 1648: 50 5S 309-310
2:331 Novus Atlas and Atlas Major (Vierter Teil), J. Blaeu, 1645-48: 50 6O 417-418
Nuevo Atlas del Reyno de Inglaterra, J. Blaeu, 1645/48: 50 6Q 373-374

References Van der Krogt 2002 18:63.

151   [5370:1] Durham
EPISCOPATVS | DVNELMENSIS | Vulgo | The Bishoprike of |
DVRHAM
The diocese of Dunelm, in the vulgar tongue the bishopric of Durham
Amstelodami | apud Joannem Janßonium.
40.5 X 51 cm.

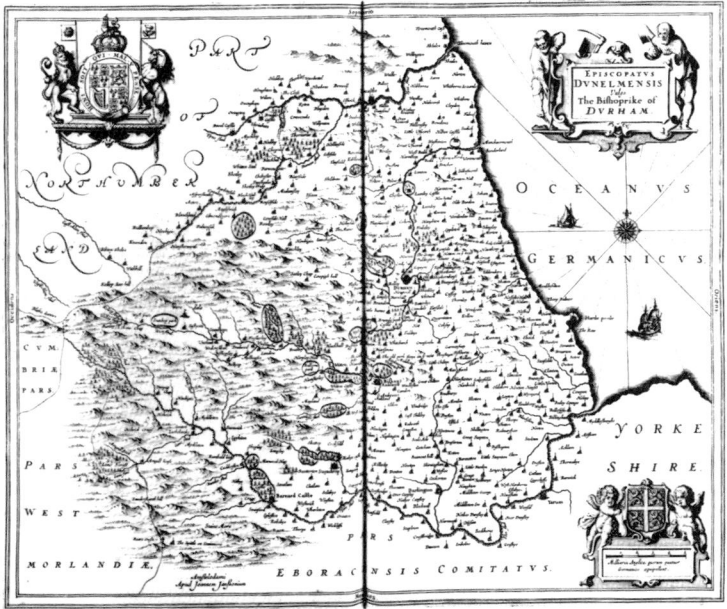

Notes   Above left is the royal coat of arms. The motto in the coat of arms is: Honi
soit qui mal y pense, which means 'Shame be to him who thinks evil of it', the motto of the Order of the Garter. Below to the right, above the scale cartouche, is the
coat of arms of Durham. The title cartouche is surrounded by images of farmers.

Occurrence in atlases
1:403/05 Atlas Novus, Janssonius, 1647/1657-62: v4 43 5Q 311-312
1:414/15 Le Nouvel Atlas... Tome Quatrieme, Janssonius, 1646-49: v4 43 5Y 329-
330
1:425 Novus Atlas, Janssonius, 1647-49: v4 43 6L 389-390
1:434/36 Nieuwen Atlas... Het Vierde deel, Janssonius, 1647-49/1658: v4 43 3O5
1:408 Atlas, Janssonius, after c. 1680: v3 42

152 [5370:2] Durham
EPISCOPATVS | DVNELMENSIS. | Vulgo | The Bishoprike of | DVRHAM
The diocese of Dunelm, in the vulgar tongue the bishopric of Durham
38 x 50 cm.

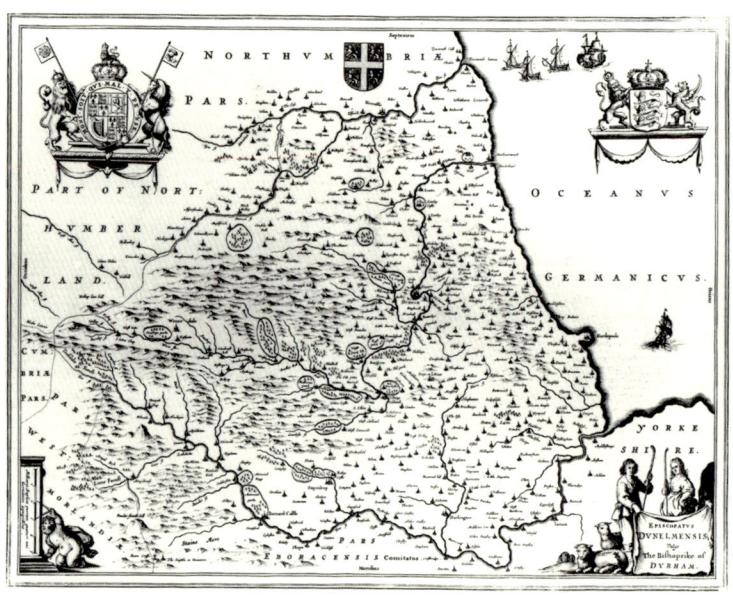

Notes   The map has been copied from Speed's *Theatre*, edition after 1623, and was specially made for the atlas of England, which Joan Blaeu in 1645 joined as a fourth part to his *Atlas novus*.

Occurrence in atlases

2:301 Theatrum Orbis Terrarum sive Atlas Novus Pars Quarta, J. Blaeu, 1646: 51 6S 397-398

2:302-3 Theatrum Orbis Terrarum sive Atlas Novus Pars Quarta, J. Blaeu, 1646-48: 51 6G 345-346

2:311 Le Theatre du Monde ou Nouvel Atlas, Quatriesme Partie, J. Blaeu: 51 5X 337-338

2:312 Cinquème Volume de la Geographie Blaviane, J. Blaeu, 1663-67: 51 5N 283-284

2:321 Toonneel des Aerdycks oft Nieuwe Atlas... Vierde deel, J. Blaeu, 1648: 51 6L 371-372

2:322 Toonneel des Aerdycks oft Nieuwe Atlas... Vierde deel, J. Blaeu, 1648: 51 5X 317-318

2:331 Novus Atlas and Atlas Major (Vierter Teil), J. Blaeu, 1645-48: 51 6R 427-428

Nuevo Atlas del Reyno de Inglaterra, J. Blaeu, 1645/48: 51 6T 383-384

References   Van der Krogt 2002 18:64.

153   [5370:373] Durham
Dunelmensis | Episcopatus.
The Diocese of Durham
8.5 X 12 cm.

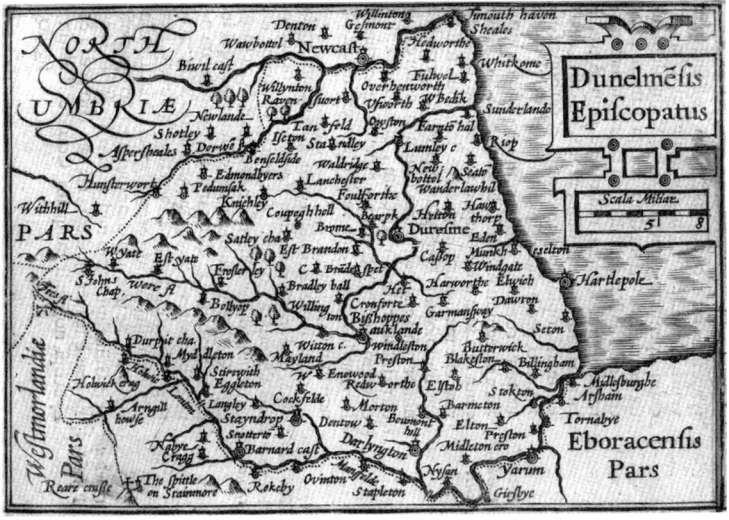

Notes   This map is from a collection of 44 maps of the British Isles, engraved by Pieter van den Keere. The maps are comparable in size to those of the *Tabularum Geographicarum*, published by Pieter Bertius, for which Van den Keere engraved many maps. Although the maps of Van den Keere form one collection, no title-page is known.

Occurrence in atlases
373:01 Atlas of the British Isles, Van den Keere, c. 1605: 18
373:02 Britannia, Camden, 1617: 32 2K1r 513

References   Skelton 1970, 4.

154.1 [5375:1.1] Lancashire
COMITATVS | LANCASTRENSIS. | The | COVNTIE PALATINE | of | LANCASTER
The County of Lancaster. The Palatine County Lancaster
38 x 50 cm.

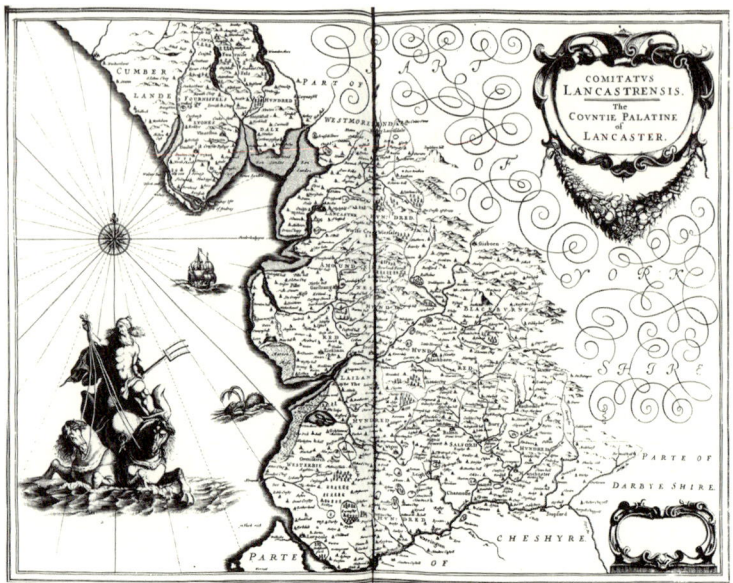

Notes On the left, in the sea, is an image of the god of the seas Neptune (or Greek, Poseidon). On the right, below, there is an empty cartouche, possibly intended for a dedication.

Occurrence in atlases

1:324 Appendix Atlantis, Janssonius, 1636: 17 Q

1:323 Newer Atlas, Janssonius, 1636: vi 19 R(Q)

1:332 Appendix Atlantis, Janssonius/Hondius, 1637: 15 T

1:421/2 Newer Atlas, Janssonius, 1638: vi 20 Q

1:431 Nieuwen Atlas, Janssonius, 1638-44: vi 19 2A(T)

1:434/36 Nieuwen Atlas... Het Vierde deel, Janssonius, 1647-49/1658: v4 44 3O6

154.2 [5375:1.2] Lancashire
LANCASTRIA | PALATINATVS | Anglis | LANCASTER & |
LANCAS SHIRE
Palatinate Lancaster. English Lancaster and Lancashire
Amstelodami | apud Joannem Janßonium.

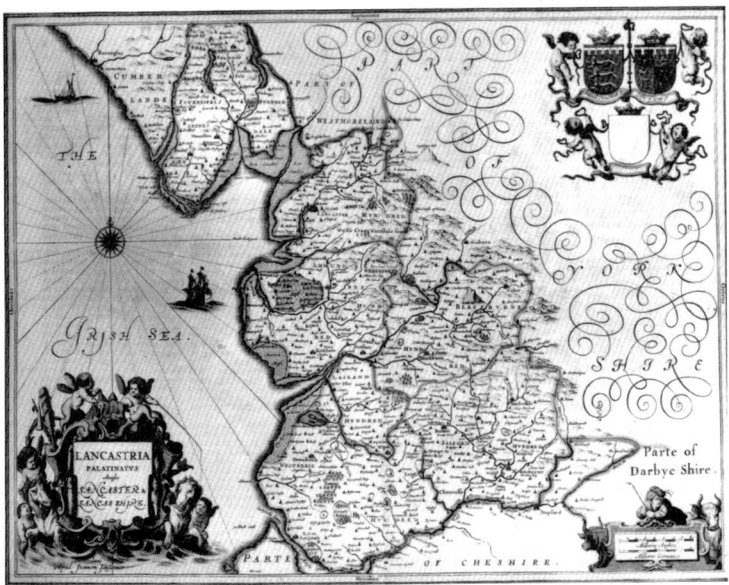

Notes   Above right there are three coats of arms of noble families, surrounded
by putti. One of the coats of arms is empty.

Occurrence in atlases
1:403/05 Atlas Novus, Janssonius, 1647/1657-62: v4 44 5S 317-318
1:414/15 Le Nouvel Atlas... Tome Quatrieme, Janssonius, 1646-49: v4 44 6A 333-
334
1:425 Novus Atlas, Janssonius, 1647-49: v4 44 6N 395-396
1:434/36 Nieuwen Atlas... Het Vierde deel, Janssonius, 1647-49/1658: v4 44 3O6
1:408 Atlas, Janssonius, after c. 1680: v3 43

155   [5375:2] Lancashire
**LANCASTRIA | PALATINATVS | Anglis | LANCASTER et |
Lancas shire**
Palatinate Lancaster, in English Lancaster and Lancashire
39.5 X 51 cm.

Notes   The coat of arms of Lancaster, placed above the title, has not been filled
in. Beside the title stand the coats of arms of Edmund 'Crouchback' (1244–1296)
of the house of Plantagenet, the first earl of Lancaster, and of John of Gaunt
(1340–1399), duke of Lancaster,. A third coat of arms has remained empty. The
map has been copied from Speed's *Theatre*, edition after 1623, and was specially
made for the atlas of England, which Joan Blaeu in 1645 joined as a fourth part
to his *Atlas novus*.

Occurrence in atlases

2:301 Theatrum Orbis Terrarum sive Atlas Novus Pars Quarta, J. Blaeu, 1646: 52
        6V 403-404

2:302-3 Theatrum Orbis Terrarum sive Atlas Novus Pars Quarta, J. Blaeu, 1646-
48: 52 6I 349-350

2:311 Le Theatre du Monde ou Nouvel Atlas, Quatriesme Partie, J. Blaeu: 52 5Z
341-342

2:312 Cinquème Volume de la Geographie Blaviane, J. Blaeu, 1663-67: 52 5P 287-
288

2:321 Toonneel des Aerdycks oft Nieuwe Atlas... Vierde deel, J. Blaeu, 1648: 52
6N 375-376

2:322 Toonneel des Aerdycks oft Nieuwe Atlas... Vierde deel, J. Blaeu, 1648: 52
5Z 321-322

2:331 Novus Atlas and Atlas Major (Vierter Teil), J. Blaeu, 1645-48: 52 6T 433-434

Nuevo Atlas del Reyno de Inglaterra, J. Blaeu, 1645/48: 52 6X 389-390

References   Van der Krogt 2002 18:65.

156   [5375:373] Lancashire
Lancaster
8.5 x 12 cm.

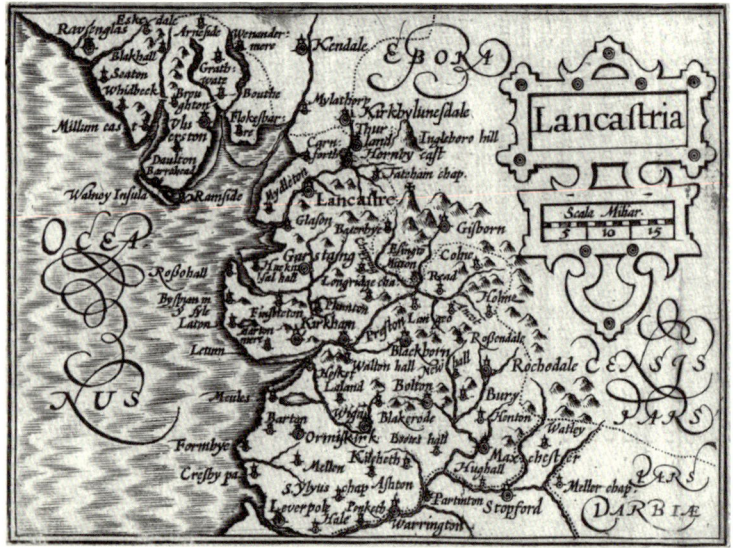

Notes   This map is from a collection of 44 maps of the British Isles, engraved by Pieter van den Keere. The maps are comparable in size to those of the *Tabularum Geographicarum*, published by Pieter Bertius, for which Van den Keere engraved many maps. Although the maps of Van den Keere form one collection, no title-page is known.

Occurrence in atlases
373:01 Atlas of the British Isles, Van den Keere, c. 1605: 21
373:02 Britannia, Camden, 1617: 33 2K6r 523

References   Skelton 1970, 4.

157   [5380:2] Westmorland
WESTMORIA | COMITATVS; | Anglice | WESTMORLAND
The county of Westmoria; English Westmorland
38 x 50 cm.

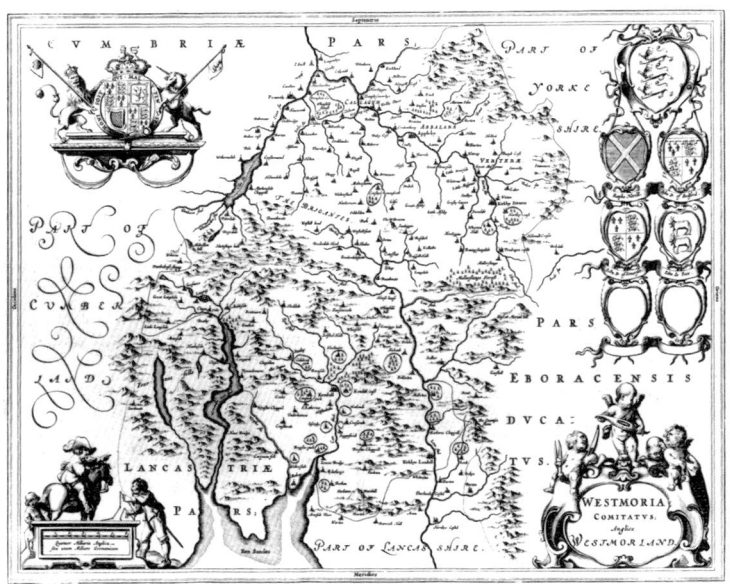

Notes   The coats of arms of the lords of Westmorland are as it were hanging from the coat of arms of England. The map has been copied from Speed's *Theatre*, edition after 1623, and was specially made for the atlas of England, which Joan Blaeu in 1645 joined as a fourth part to his *Atlas novus*.

Occurrence in atlases

2:301 Theatrum Orbis Terrarum sive Atlas Novus Pars Quarta, J. Blaeu, 1646: 53 6Z 411-412

2:302-3 Theatrum Orbis Terrarum sive Atlas Novus Pars Quarta, J. Blaeu, 1646-48: 53 6M 357-358

2:311 Le Theatre du Monde ou Nouvel Atlas, Quatriesme Partie, J. Blaeu: 53 6B 345-346

2:312 Cinquème Volume de la Geographie Blaviane, J. Blaeu, 1663-67: 53 5R 291-292

2:321 Toonneel des Aerdycks oft Nieuwe Atlas... Vierde deel, J. Blaeu, 1648: 53 6P 381-382

2:322 Toonneel des Aerdycks oft Nieuwe Atlas... Vierde deel, J. Blaeu, 1648: 53 6B 327-328

2:331 Novus Atlas and Atlas Major (Vierter Teil), J. Blaeu, 1645-48: 53 6Y 441-442

Nuevo Atlas del Reyno de Inglaterra, J. Blaeu, 1645/48: 53 7A 397-398

References   Van der Krogt 2002 18:66.

158   [5380:373] Westmoreland and Cumberland
Westmorlandia | et | Comberlandia.
Westmorland and Cumberland
8.5 x 12 cm.

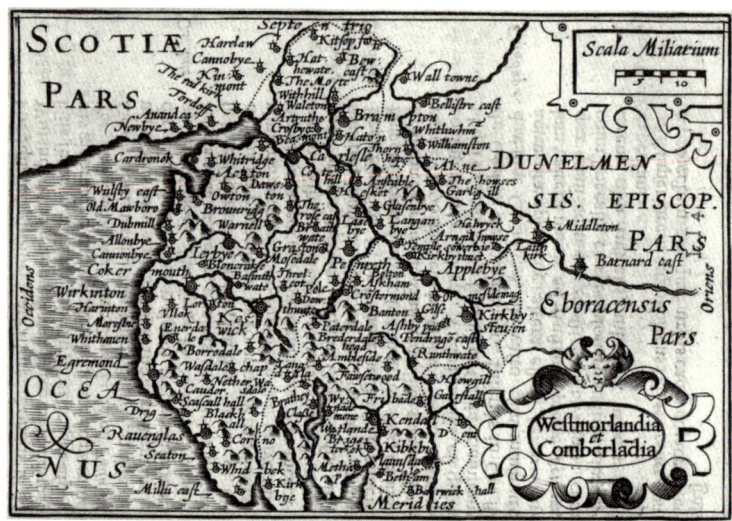

Notes   This map is from a collection of 44 maps of the British Isles, engraved by
Pieter van den Keere. The maps are comparable in size to those of the *Tabularum
Geographicarum*, published by Pieter Bertius, for which Van den Keere engraved
many maps. Although the maps of Van den Keere form one collection, no title-
page is known.

Occurrence in atlases
373:01 Atlas of the British Isles, Van den Keere, c. 1605: 20
373:02 Britannia, Camden, 1617: 34 2L4r 535

References   Skelton 1970, 4.

159   [5385:1] Cumberland
CUMBRIA & | WESTMORIA. | Vulgo | Cumberland & West- |
morland
Cumbria and Westmoria, in the vulgar tongue Cumberland and
Westmorland
Amstelodami | apud Joannem Janßonium.
42.5 X 54 cm.

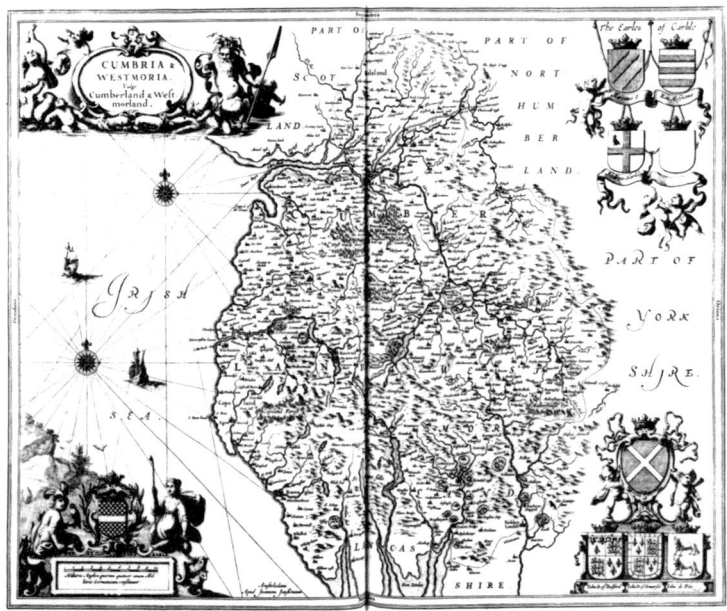

Notes   The map is dedicated to Henry Clifford (1591–1643), the 5th and last earl
of Cumberland. After 1643 Cumberland became a duchy.

Occurrence in atlases
1:403/05 Atlas Novus, Janssonius, 1647/1657-62: v4 45 5^V 323-324
1:414/15 Le Nouvel Atlas... Tome Quatrieme, Janssonius, 1646-49: v4 45 6C 337-
338
1:425 Novus Atlas, Janssonius, 1647-49: v4 45 6Q 403-404
1:434/36 Nieuwen Atlas... Het Vierde deel, Janssonius, 1647-49/1658: v4 45 3^P
163-164
1:408 Atlas, Janssonius, after c. 1680: v3 44

160   [5385:2] Cumberland
CVMBRIA; | Vulgo | CUMBERLAND
Cumbria, in the vulgar tongue Cumberland
41 X 49.5 cm.

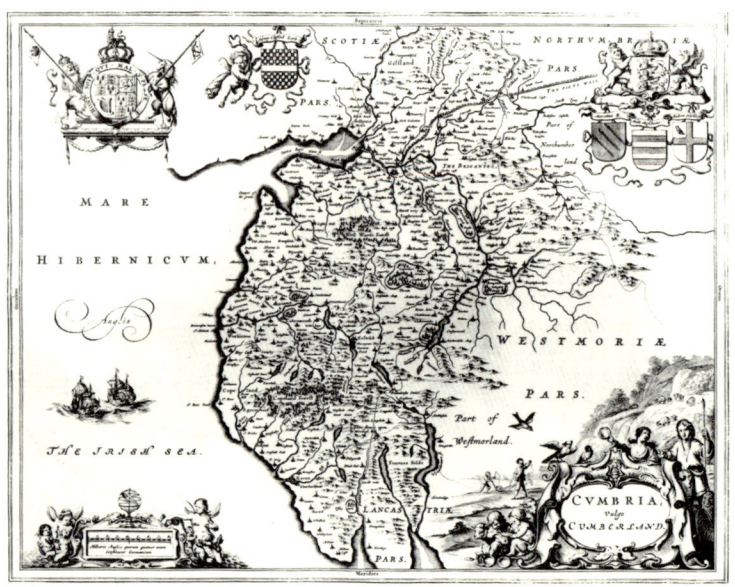

Notes   The title cartouche is surrounded by a rural scene with farmers and shepherds with their sheep on a slope, presumably a reproduction of the mountainous Lake District. Above the map card, the royal coat of arms and some coats of arms of the earls of Cumberland are drawn. The map has been copied from Speed's *Theatre*, edition after 1623, and was specially made for the atlas of England, which Joan Blaeu in 1645 joined as a fourth part to his *Atlas novus*.

Occurrence in atlases   2:301 Theatrum Orbis Terrarum sive Atlas Novus Pars
Quarta, J. Blaeu, 1646: 54 7B 415-416
2:302-3 Theatrum Orbis Terrarum sive Atlas Novus Pars Quarta, J. Blaeu, 1646-48: 54 6N 359-360
2:311 Le Theatre du Monde ou Nouvel Atlas, Quatriesme Partie, J. Blaeu: 54 6C 347-348
2:312 Cinquème Volume de la Geographie Blaviane, J. Blaeu, 1663-67: 54 5S 293-294
2:321 Toonneel des Aerdycks oft Nieuwe Atlas... Vierde deel, J. Blaeu, 1648: 54 6R 385-386
2:322 Toonneel des Aerdycks oft Nieuwe Atlas... Vierde deel, J. Blaeu, 1648: 54 6C 329-330
2:331 Novus Atlas and Atlas Major (Vierter Teil), J. Blaeu, 1645-48: 54 6Z 443-444
Nuevo Atlas del Reyno de Inglaterra, J. Blaeu, 1645/48: 54 7C 401-402

References   Van der Krogt 2002 18:67.

161.1   [5385:352.1] Cumberland
CVMBRIÆ | COMITATVS | Descriptio.
Map of the county of Cumberland
15 X 20 cm.

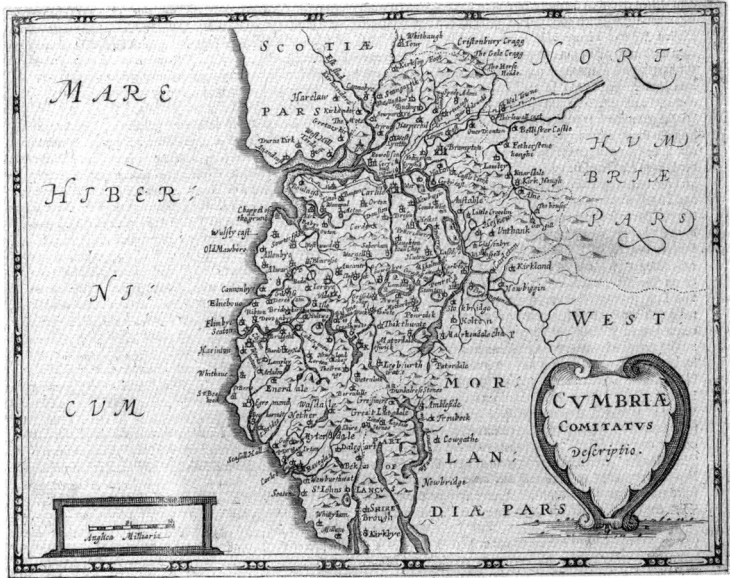

Notes   The boundaries formed in the twelfth century did not change substantial-
ly over the county's existence. It bordered four English counties and two Scottish
counties. These were Northumberland and County Durham to the east; Westmorland to the south, the Furness part of Lancashire to the southwest; Dumfriesshire
to the north and Roxburghshire to the northeast.

Occurrence in atlases
352:32/33 Atlas Minor, Janssonius, 1648-51: VI 7 D2r 27

161.2 [5385:352.2] Cumberland
Comté de | CUMBERLAND.
The county of Cumberland

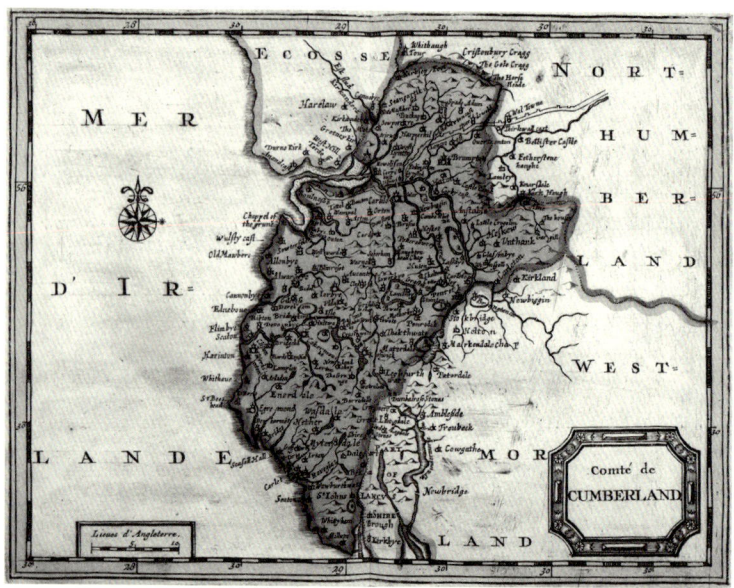

Notes   This map appeared in the *Atlas soulagé de son gros & pesant fardeau*, published by Pieter van der Aa. Almost all the maps are printed from reworked plates of Janssonius's *Atlas Minor*. The titles and scale were translated into French. Several Latin texts on the maps have been removed, as have the Latin names of the wind directions in the borders. The cartouches have been modernized and windroses added. Other modernizations are the removal of ships and sea monsters, and erasing names in curled letters and replacing them with Roman type letters. Latin names of seas and countries are often translated into French.

Occurrence in atlases

352:51.2-9 Atlas soulagé..., Van der Aa, c. 1714: v4 14 blank

162.1 **[5390:1.1] Northumberland**
Comitatus | NORTHVM- | BRIA
The county of Northumberland
41 X 49 cm.

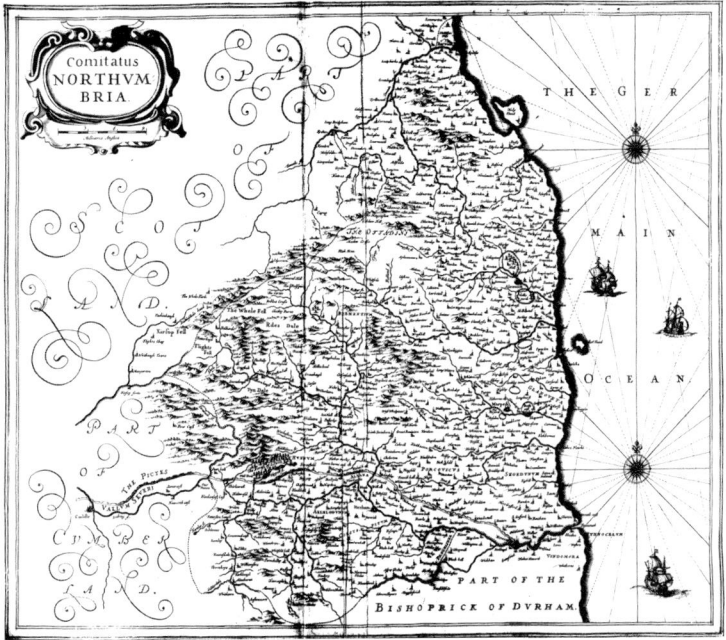

Notes   This first state of Janssonius' map of Northumberland has the title cartouche in the corner above left. The map does not have a scale cartouche.

Occurrence in atlases
1:432 Des Nieuwen Atlantis Aenhang, Janssonius, 1644: 1 a
1:434/36 Nieuwen Atlas... Het Vierde deel, Janssonius, 1647-49/1658: v4 46 3R

162.2 [5390:1.2] Northumberland

COMITATVS | NORTHVMBRIA. | vernacule | NORTHUMBER | LAND

The county of Northumbria, vernacularly Northumberland

Amstelodami | apud Joannem Janßonium.

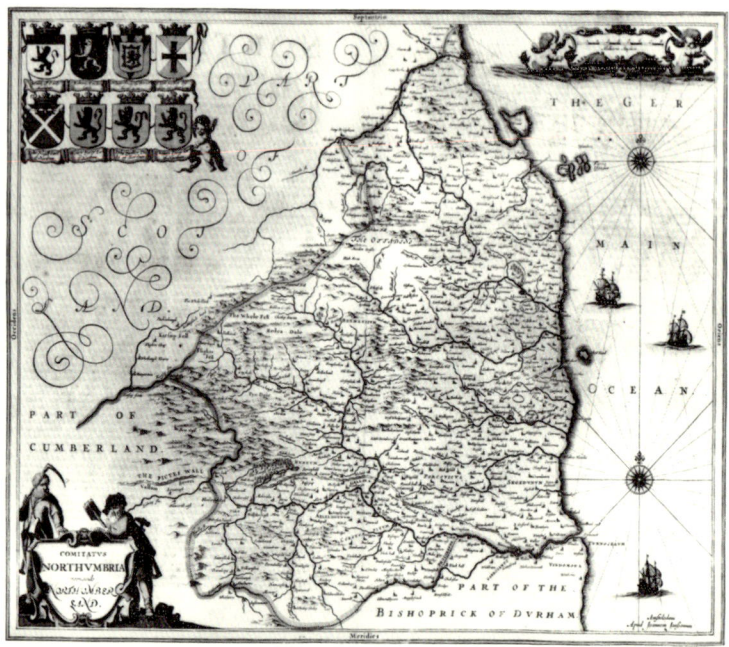

Notes This second state of the map of Northumberland contains eight coats of arms of noble families, the title cartouche is surrounded by images of farmers and there is a scale cartouche.

Occurrence in atlases

1:403/05 Atlas Novus, Janssonius, 1647/1657-62: v4 46 6B 339-340

1:414/15 Le Nouvel Atlas... Tome Quatrieme, Janssonius, 1646-49: v4 46 6H 353-354

1:425 Novus Atlas, Janssonius, 1647-49: v4 46 6X 421-422

1:434/36 Nieuwen Atlas... Het Vierde deel, Janssonius, 1647-49/1658: v4 46 3R

1:408 Atlas, Janssonius, after c. 1680: v3 46

163   [5390:2] Northumberland
COMITATVS | NORTHVMBRIA; | Vernacule | NORTHUMBER-
LAND
The county of Northumbria, vernacularly Northumberland
Ioh: Blaeu Exc.
41 X 50 cm.

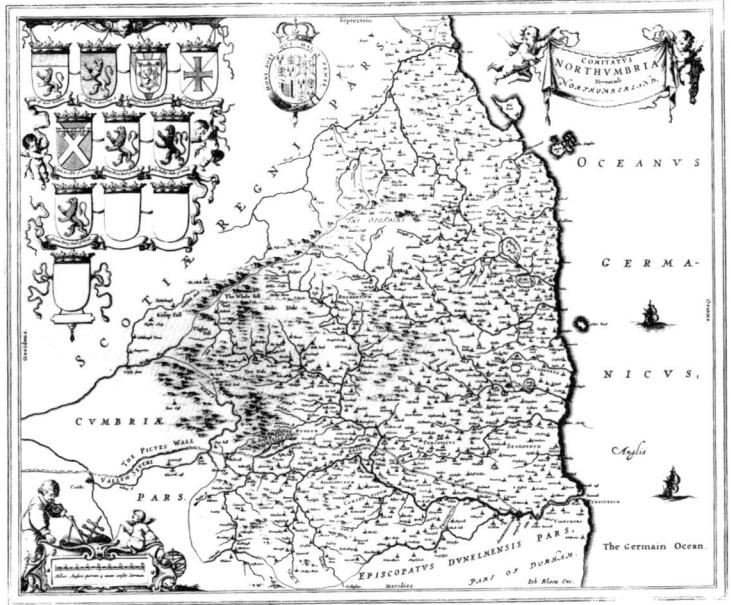

Notes   On the left are the coats of arms of the earls of Northumberland. The
map has been copied from Speed's *Theatre*, edition after 1623, and was specially
made for the atlas of England, which Joan Blaeu in 1645 joined as a fourth part
to his *Atlas novus*.

Occurrence in atlases   2:301 Theatrum Orbis Terrarum sive Atlas Novus Pars
   Quarta, J. Blaeu, 1646: 55 7F 429-430
2:302-3 Theatrum Orbis Terrarum sive Atlas Novus Pars Quarta, J. Blaeu, 1646-48:
55 6R 367-368; 373-374
2:311 Le Theatre du Monde ou Nouvel Atlas, Quatriesme Partie, J. Blaeu: 55 6G 361-362
2:312 Cinquème Volume de la Geographie Blaviane, J. Blaeu, 1663-67: 55 5X 303-304
2:321 Toonneel des Aerdycks oft Nieuwe Atlas... Vierde deel, J. Blaeu, 1648: 55
6X 395-396
2:322 Toonneel des Aerdycks oft Nieuwe Atlas... Vierde deel, J. Blaeu, 1648: 55
6G 341-342
2:331 Novus Atlas and Atlas Major (Vierter Teil), J. Blaeu, 1645-48: 55 7E 461-462
Nuevo Atlas del Reyno de Inglaterra, J. Blaeu, 1645/48: 55 7H 417-418

References   Van der Krogt 2002 18:68.

164 [5390:373] Northumberland
NORTHUMBRIA.
Northumbria
8.5 x 12 cm.

Notes This map is from a collection of 44 maps of the British Isles, engraved by Pieter van den Keere. The maps are comparable in size to those of the *Tabularum Geographicarum*, published by Pieter Bertius, for which Van den Keere engraved many maps. Although the maps of Van den Keere form one collection, no title-page is known.

Occurrence in atlases
373:01 Atlas of the British Isles, Van den Keere, c. 1605: 19
373:02 Britannia, Camden, 1617: 35 2M6r 555

References Skelton 1970, 4.

References

Broecke, M.P.R van den (2011), *Ortelius Atlas Maps. An illustrated Guide Second revised edition*. Houten: HES & DE GRAAF Publishers.

Karrow, R.W. (1993), *Mapmakers of the sixteenth century and their maps. Bibliographies of the Cartographers of Abraham Ortelius, 1570*. Chicago: Newberry Library / Speculum Orbis Press.

Krogt, P. van der & E. de Groot (2002), *The Atlas Blaeu-van der Hem of the Austrian National Library. Volume III British Isles, northern and eastern Europe. Descriptive catalogue of volumes 9-17 of the Atlas*. 't Goy-Houten: HES & DE GRAAF Publishers.

Meurer, P. (1991), *Fontes cartographici Orteliani : das 'Theatrum orbis terrarum' von Abraham Ortelius und seine Kartenquellen*. Weinheim: VCH, Acta Humaniora

Schilder, G. (1993), *Monumenta Cartographica Neerlandica IV*. Alphen aan den Rijn: Uitgeverij Canaletto.

Shirley, R.W. (1991), *Early printed maps of the British Isles 1477-1650. The completely revised and updated edition*. East Grinstead: Antique Atlas Publications.

Skelton, R.A. (1970), *County Atlases of the British Isles 1579-1703*. London: Carta Press.

Werner, J. (1998), *Abraham Ortelius (1527-1598): aartsvader van onze atlas*. Amsterdam: Universiteitsbibliotheek.

Index to personal names

The numbers refer to the map numbers.

Index to geographical names

The numbers refer to the map numbers.

Index to map titles

The numbers refer to the map numbers.

List of atlases

The number noted before the atlas title refers to the *Atlantes Neerlandici*, in which more information about each atlas can be found.

MERCATOR'S ATLAS

1:011 *Atlas*, Mercator's heirs 1595
1:012 *Atlas*, Mercator's heirs 1602

THE MERCATOR-HONDIUS ATLAS

1:101 *Atlas*, Hondius and Claesz. 1606
1:102 *Atlas,* Hondius and Claesz. 1607-08
1:103 *Atlas*, Hondius 1611-12
1:104 *Atlas*, Hondius Jr. 1613-19
1:105 *Atlas*, Hondius 1623
1:107 *Atlas*, Hondius 1630
1:111 *Atlas,* Hondius 1609
1:112 *Atlas*, Hondius Jr. 1613-16
1:113 *Atlas*, Hondius Jr. 1619
1:114 *Atlas*, Hondius 1628

APPENDICES AND THEATRI

1:202 *Appendix*, Janssonius 1630
1:203 *Appendix*, Hondius 1631

THE MERCATOR-HONDIUS ATLAS, 1633-38

1:301 *Appendix Novi Atlantis,* Janssonius 1637
1:311 *Atlas*, Hondius 1633
1:312 *L'Appendice de l'Atlas,* Hondius 1633
1:321/22 *Atlas*, Janssonius and/or Hondius 1633
1:323 *Newer Atlas* Janssonius 1636
1:324 *Appendix Atlantis,* Janssonius 1636
1:331 *Atlas,* Janssonius and/or Hondius 1634
1:332 *Appendix Atlantis,* Janssonius and Hondius 1637
1:341 *Atlas,* Hondius and Janssonius 1636-41

THE ATLAS NOVUS

Latin editions, 1638-c.1680

1:401 *Atlas Novus*, Janssonius and Hondius 1638
1:403 *Atlas Novus*, Janssonius 1647

1:404 *Atlas Novus,* Janssonius 1649-56
1:405 *Atlas Novus,* Janssonius 1657-62
1:407 *Atlas Contractus,* Janssonius Heirs 1666
1:408 *Atlas,* Janssonius after c. 1680

French editions, 1639-1658

1:411 *Nouveau Theatre du Monde,* Hondius 1639-42
1:413 *Nouveau Theatre du Monde,* Janssonius 1644-47
1:414 *Le Nouvel Atlas... Tome Quatrieme,* Janssonius 1646
1:415 *Nouvel Atlas,* Janssonius 1646-49

German editions, 1638-c.1690

1:421 *Newer Atlas,* Janssonius 1638
1:424 *Novus Atlas,* Janssonius 1644-45
1:425 *Novus Atlas,* Janssonius 1647-49

Dutch editions, 1638-1658

1:431 *Nieuwen Atlas,* Janssonius 1638-44
1:432 *Des Nieuwen Atlantis Aenhang,* Janssonius, 1644
1:433 *Nieuwen Atlas,* Janssonius 1645-47
1:434 *Nieuwen Atlas... Het Vierde Deel,* Janssonius 1647-49
1:435 *Nieuwen Atlas* in five volumes, Johannes Janssonius 1652-53
1:436 *Nieuwen Atlas,* Janssonius 1658

Spanish editions, 1653-66

1:441 *Nuevo Atlas,* Janssonius 1653-66

WILLEM BLAEU'S APPENDIX

2:021 *Appendix Theatri... et Atlantis,* Willem Jansz. Blaeu 1631
2:022 *Appendix Theatri... et Atlantis,* Willem Jansz. Blaeu 1631

THEATRUM ORBIS TERRARUM

Latin edition

2:101 *Theatrum Orbis Terrarum,* Willem and Joan Blaeu 1635

French edition

2:111 *Le Theatre du Monde,* Willem and Joan Blaeu 1635

Dutch edition

2:121 *Toonneel des Aerdrycks,* Willem and Joan Blaeu 1635

German editions

2:131 *Novus Atlas,* Willem Jansz. Blaeu 1634/35
2:132 *Novus Atlas,* Willem Jansz. Blaeu 1635

THEATRUM ORBIS TERRARUM IN THREE TO SIX VOLUMES
Latin editions
2:201 *Theatrum Orbis Terrarum,* Willem and Joan Blaeu 1640
2:202 *Theatrum Orbis Terrarum,* Joan Blaeu 1644-45
2:203 *Theatrum Orbis Terrarum,* Joan Blaeu 1649-55

French editions
2:211 *Theatre du Monde ou Nouvel Atlas,* Joan and Cornelis Blaeu 1640-43 (1638)
2:212 *Theatre du Monde ou Nouvel Atlas,* Joan Blaeu 1643-45
2:213 *Theatre du Monde ou Nouvel Atlas,* Joan Blaeu 1645-50

Dutch edition
2:221 *Toonneel des Aerdrycks,* Joan and Cornelis Blaeu 1642-43

German editions
2:231 *Novus Atlas,* Joan and Cornelis Blaeu 1641-42
2:232 *Novus Atlas,* Joan Blaeu 1647-49

THE ATLAS OF ENGLAND
Latin editions
2:301 *Theatrum Orbis Terrarum sive Atlas Novus Pars Quarta,* Joan Blaeu 1645 and 1646
2:302 *Theatrum Orbis Terrarum sive Atlas Novus Pars Quarta,* Joan Blaeu 1646 and 1648
2:303 *Geographiæ Blavianæ Volumen Quintum,* Joan Blaeu 1662

French editions
2:311 *Le Theatre du Monde ou Nouvel Atlas... Quatriesme Partie,* Joan Blaeu 1645-48
2:312 *Cinquiéme Volume de la Geographie Blaviane,* Joan Blaeu 1663 and 1667

Dutch edition
2:321 *Toonneel des Aerdrycks oft Nieuwe Atlas... Vierde Deel,* Joan Blaeu 1646 [1647]-1648
2:322 *Toonneel des Aerdrycks oft Nieuwe Atlas... Vierde Deel,* and *Vierde Stuck der Aerdrycksbeschryving,* Joan Blaeu 1648

German editions
2:331 *Novus Atlas* and *Atlas Major (Vierter Theil),* Joan Blaeu 1645-48

Spanish edition
2:341 Nuevo Atlas del Reyno de Inglaterra, Joan Blaeu 1658/62

THE THEATRUM ORBIS TERRARUM BY ABRAHAM ORTELIUS
Latin editions
31:001 Theatrum Orbis Terrarum, Coppens van Diest, 1570

31:002 *Theatrum Orbis Terrarum,* Coppens van Diest, 1571

31:010 *Additamentum Theatri Orbis Terrarum,* [Coppens van Diest], 1573

31:011 *Theatrum Orbis Terrarum,* Coppens van Diest, 1573

31:012 *Theatrum Orbis Terrarum,* Coppens van Diest, 1574

31:013 *Theatrum Orbis Terrarum,* Van Den Rade, 1575

31:021 *Theatrum Orbis Terrarum,* Plantin, 1579

31:022 *Theatrum Orbis Terrarum,* (2nd printing), Plantin, 1579

31:031 *Theatrum Orbis Terrarum,* Plantin, 1584

31:041 *Theatrum Orbis Terrarum,* Plantin, 1592

31:051 *Theatrum Orbis Terrarum,* Plantin, 1595

31:052 *Theatrum Orbis Terrarum,* Moretus, 1601

31:053 *Theatrum Orbis Terrarum,* Vrients, 1603

31:054 *Theatrum Orbis Terrarum,* Vrients, 1609

31:055 *Theatrum Orbis Terrarum,* J. & B. Moretus, 1612

Dutch editions
31:101 *Theatre oft Toonneel des Aerdtbodems*, Coppens van Diest, 1571

31:111 *Theatre oft Toonneel des Aerdtbodems*, Coppens van Diest, 1571 [1573]

31:121 *Theatrum Orbis Terrarum,* [Claesz.], 1598

31:122 *Theatrum Orbis Terrarum,* Jan Moretus's widow and sons, 1598 [1613]

German editions
31:201 *Theatrum oder Schawplatz des Erdbodems*, Coppens van Diest, 1572

31:210 *Ein Zusatz bei dass Theatrum*, [Coppens van Diest], 1573

31:211 *Theatrum oder Schawplatz des Erdbodems*, Coppens van Diest, 1573/72

31:221 *Theatrum oder Schawbüch des Erdtkreijs*, Plantin, 1580

31:222 *Theatrum oder Schawbüch des Erdtkreijs*, Plantin, 1580 [1589]

31:251 *Theatrum oder Schawbuch der gantzen Welt*, [Vrients], 1602

31:290 *Theatrum Orbis Terrarum*, Koler, 1572

French editions
31:301 *Théâtre de l'Univers,* Coppens van Diest, 1572

31:310 *Addition du Théâtre de l'Univers,* [Coppens van Diest], 1574

31:311 *Théâtre de l'Univers,* Coppens van Diest, 1574/72

31:321 *Théâtre de l'Univers,* Plantin, 1581

31:331 *Théâtre de l'Univers,* Plantin, 1587

31:351 *Théâtre de l'Univers,* Plantin, 1598

Spanish editions
31:431 *Theatro de la Tierra Universal*, Plantin, 1588

31:451 Theatro d'el Orbe de la Tierra, Vrients, 1602

31:452 Theatro d'el Orbe de la Tierra, Vrients, 1609

31:454 *Theatro d'el Orbe de la Tierra*Balthasar II Moretus, 1612 [1641]

English edition
31:551 The Theatre of the Whole World, Norton, 1606

Italian editions
31:651 Theatro del Mondo, Vrients, 1608
31:652 *Theatro del Mondo,* J. & B. Moretus, 1612

THE SPECULUM ORBIS TERRARUM BY GERARD EN CORNELIS DE JODE
32:01 *Speculum Orbis Terrarum,* De Jode, 1578
32:02 *Speculum Orbis Terrae,* De Jode, 1593

THE SPIEGHEL DER WERELD BY FILIPS GALLE
331:01 *Spieghel der Werelt,* Heyns, 1577
331:02 *Spieghel der Werelt,* Heyns, 1583
331:03 *Spieghel der Werelt,* Heyns, 1596
331:11 *Le Miroir du Monde,* Heyns, 1579
331:12 *Le Miroir du Monde,* Heyns, 1583
331:21 *Theatri Orbis Terrarum Enchiridion,* Favoli, 1585

THE EPITOME BY FILIPS GALLE
332:01 *Epitome du Théâtre du Monde,* Galle, 1588
332:02 *Epitome du Théâtre du Monde,* Galle, 1590
332:03 *Epitome du Théâtre du Monde,* Galle, 1598
332:04 *Abrégé du Théâtre d'Ortelius,* Vrients, 1602
332:11 *Epitome Theatri Orteliani,* Galle, 1589
332:12 *Epitome Theatri Orteliani,* Galle, 1595
332:13 *Epitome Theatri Orteliani,* Vrients, 1601
332:21 *Theatro d'Abrahamo Ortelio,* Galle, 1593
332:22 *Breve Compendio dal Theatro Orteliano,* Vrients, 1602
332:31 *An Epitome of Ortelius his Theatre,* Norton, [1602]

THE EPITOME BY JAN VAN KEERBERGEN
333:01 *Epitome Theatri Orbis Terrarum,* Van Keerbergen, 1601
333:02 *Epitome Theatri Orbis Terrarum,* Vrients, 1609
333:03 *Epitome Theatri Orbis Terrarum,* Plantin, 1612
333:11 *L'Epitome du Théâtre de l'Univers,* Van Keerbergen, 1602
333:21 *Breve Compendio dal Theatro Orteliano,* Vrients, 1602
333:22 *Compendio dal Theatro del Mondo,* Plantin's Bookshop, 1612
333:31 *Epitome of the Theater of the Worlde,* Shawe, 1603
333:41 *Auszug auß des Abrahami Ortely Theatro Orbis,* Hulsius, 1604

THE MIROIR DU MONDE AND NEDERLANDTSCHEN LANDT-SPIEGEL BY ZACHARIAS HEYNS

334:01 *Le Miroir du Monde*, Heyns, 1598

THE CAERT-THRESOOR BY BARENT LANGENES AND CORNELIS CLAESZ.

Dutch editions

341:01 *Caert-Thresoor*, Langenes, 1598

341:02 *Caert-Thresoor*, Claesz, 1599

341:03 *Hand-boeck of Cort Begrijp der Caerten*, Claesz., 1609

French editions

341:11 *Thrésor de Chartes*, Claesz., c. 1600

341:12 *Thrésor de Chartes,* Claesz., 1602

341:13 Thrésor de Chartes, Laurensz., c. 1609

Bertius's Tabulae Geopgraphicae Contractae by Cornelis Claesz.

341:51 Tabulae Geographicae Contractae, Bertius, 1600

341:52 Tabulae Geographicae Contractae, Editio Secunda, Bertius, 1602/03

341:53 Tabulae Geographicae Contractae, Editio Tertia, Bertius, 1606

341:54 *Tabulae Geographicae Contractae,* Claes Jansz. Visscher, 1649

German edition

341:61 Geographischer eyn oder zusammengezogener Tabeln, Bertius, 1612

341:62 Beschreibung der gantzen Welt, Bertius, 1650

Bertius's Tabulae Geopgraphicae Contractae by Jodocus Hondius jr.

342:01 Tabulae Geographicae Contractae, Bertius, 1616/18

342:11 La Geographie Racourcie de Pierre Bertius, Hondius, Jr., 1618

342:21 *Atlas Minor,* Joan Blaeu, 1637

MERCATOR'S ATLAS MINOR BY CORNELIS CLAESZ. AND JODO-CUS HONDIUS

Latin editions

351:01 *Atlas Minor,* Hondius, with Claesz. and Jansz., [1607]

351:02 *Atlas Minor,* Hondius, with Claesz. and Jan Jansz., 1610

351:03 *Atlas Minor,* Jansz., 1620-21

French editions

351:11 *Atlas Minor*, Hondius, with Claesz. and Jansz., 1608

351:12 *Atlas Minor*, Hondius, with Claesz. and Jansz., 1613

351:13 *Atlas Minor*, Hondius, with Claesz. and Jansz., 1614

German edition

351:21 *Atlas Minor*, Hondius, with Claesz. and Jansz., 1609

English edition

351:31 *Historia Mundi or Mercator's Atlas*, Cotes, 1635-39

MERCATOR'S ATLAS MINOR BY JOHANNES JANSSONIUS

Latin, French and Dutch editions

352:01 *Atlas Minor,* Janssonius, 1628

352:02 *Atlas Minor,* Janssonius, 1634

352:11 *Atlas Minor*, Janssonius, 1630

352:21 *Atlas Minor*, Janssonius, 1630

German editions

352:31 *Atlas Minor*, Janssonius, 1631

352:32 *Atlas Minor*, Janssonius, 1648-51

352:33 *Atlas Minor*, Janssonius, 1651

Van der Aa's edition

352:51 *Nouveau Petit Atlas* and *Atlas soulagé de son gros & pesant fardeau*, Van der Aa, c. 1714

MERCATOR'S ATLAS BY JAN EVERTSZ. CLOPPENBURCH

353:01 *Atlas*, Evertsz. Cloppenburch, 1630

353:02 *Atlas,* Evertsz. Cloppenburch, 1636

353:11 *Atlas,* Evertsz. Cloppenburch, 1632

353:21 *Atlas,* Janssonius van Waesbergen, 1673

353:31 *Nieuwe en beknopte Uytbeeldinge en Vertooninge der gantscher Aerdbodem,* Janssonius van Waesbergen, 1676

353:41 *Atlas portatif composé de CCLXXXV cartes,* Du Sauzet, 1734.

353:42 *Atlas portatif composé de CCLXXXV cartes,* Du Sauzet, 1734

THE ATLAS OF THE BRITISH ISLES BY PIETER VAN DEN KEERE

373:01 *Atlas of the British Isles*, Van den Keere, c. 1605

373:02 *Britannia,* Camden, 1617

MAGINI'S EDITION OF PTOLEMY'S GEOGRAPHY

381:01 *Geographiae Universae,* Keschedt and Jansz., 1597

381:03 *Geographiae, tum veteris, tum novae, volumina duo,* Jansz., 1617

Photo credits

The photographs in this volume are by courtesy of the University Library of Amsterdam, UVA, except the following: